THE RETURN OF THE PRODIGAL

and

SAUL

STANDARD EDITION
of the works of André Gide

Other volumes in the

STANDARD EDITION
of works by André Gide

Published by Secker and Warburg:

STRAIT IS THE GATE
DOSTOEVSKY
FRUITS OF THE EARTH
OEDIPUS *and* THESEUS
MARSHLANDS *and*
  PROMETHEUS MISBOUND
IF IT DIE . . .
ET NUNC MANET IN TE
  and INTIMATE JOURNAL
CORYDON

Published by Cassell & Co.:

TWO SYMPHONIES
THE COINERS
THE IMMORALIST
THE VATICAN CELLARS

*　　*　　*

Other works by André Gide:

THE JOURNALS (4 volumes)
Published by Secker and Warburg

ANDRÉ GIDE

THE RETURN OF THE PRODIGAL

Preceded by Five Other Treatises
with
SAUL
A Drama in Five Acts

Translated by
DOROTHY BUSSY

London
SECKER & WARBURG
1953

Le Retour de l'Enfant Prodigue,
précédé de cinq autres traités
Editions de la N.R.F., Marcel Rivière et Cie, 1912

Saul, Drame en cinq actes
N.R.F., copyright by Librairie Gallimard, 1912 and 1922

English Translations
first published, 1953,
by

Martin Secker & Warburg Ltd.
7 John Street, Bloomsbury,
London, W.C.1

Made and Printed in Great Britain by
The Camelot Press Ltd., London and Southampton

CONTENTS

NARCISSUS

A Treatise on the Theory of Symbolism

To Paul Valéry

Nuper me in litore vidi.

VIRGIL.

"*Le Traité du Narcisse* first appeared in 1891, in the January number of *Entretiens politiques et littéraires*; then, almost immediately afterwards, it was published in the Librairie de l'Art Indépendant." So runs André Gide's note to this Treatise in the N.R.F. (1912) edition of *Le Retour de l'Enfant prodigue, précédé de cinq autres Traités*, from which this translation—with the exception of the play *Saul*—has been made.

The date given here by the author "1891", would appear to be a misprint for "1892", for the year of its publication in book form is confirmed by Gide's entry in his *Journal* for 1910 (Vol. I, p. 268; Eng. Trans. by Justin O'Brien) under the heading "Reprinting of the *Traités*": "I beg the reader to note that the first treatise (*Le Narcisse*) dates from 1892; the second from 1893. I do not have to disavow my youthful works; but I should not wish to have them looked upon with the same eye as the products of a more mature age. I have not written a single work without having felt a profound need to write it."

This title was the first of the author's books to be published under his own name.

BOOKS are perhaps not very necessary things; a few myths were at first sufficient; a whole religion was contained in them. Peoples were astonished at the appearance of fables and without understanding worshipped; studious priests, pondering over the profundity of the images, slowly penetrated the inward meaning of the hieroglyphs. Then explanations were demanded; books amplified the myths;—but a few myths sufficed.

Thus the myth of Narcissus. *Narcissus was the perfection of beauty,—and this is why he was chaste; he disdained the nymphs—because he was in love with himself. No breath stirred the water over which he stooped tranquilly all day long to gaze at his own image. . . .*—You know the story. Nevertheless we will re-tell it. Everything has already been told; but as no one listens, we must always be beginning again.

There is no longer either a bank or a pool; no metamorphosis and no reflected flower;—nothing but Narcissus alone, nothing, therefore, but a dreaming Narcissus, isolated in the greyness of his background. In the idle monotony of the hour, he grows anxious and his doubting heart is full of questions. He wants to know, indeed, what his soul is like; it must, he feels, be adorable in the extreme, if he can judge by its long and tremulous quiverings; but his face! his image! Ah! not to know whether one loves oneself . . . to be unaware of one's own beauty! I am indistinguishable, in this featureless landscape, the planes of which nothing interrupts. Ah! to be unable to see oneself! A mirror! a mirror! a mirror! a mirror!

3

And Narcissus, who does not doubt that his form exists somewhere, rises and starts in search of the contours he longs for with which to enfold the grandeur of his soul.

On the banks of the river of Time, Narcissus has come to a stop. Fateful and illusory river where the years pass and flow away. Simple banks, like a rough setting in which the river is framed, like a glass with no quicksilver lining, where nothing is to be seen on the other side; where, on the other side, there is nothing but a stretch of empty dullness. A dismal, a lethargic canal, an almost horizontal looking-glass; and nothing would distinguish this dismal water from its colourless surroundings, but that one feels it to be flowing.

From afar, Narcissus had mistaken the river for a road, and as he was weary of being alone in all this greyness, he drew near in order to see things passing by. With his hands on the framework of the river's bank, he stoops down now in his traditional attitude. And as he gazes, suddenly, lo and behold, the water is diapered by a slight unsubstantial appearance.—River-side flowers, tree-trunks, reflected patches of blue sky, a whole swift flight of images which were only waiting for him to come into existence, and which, under his eyes, are clothed in colour. Then hills open out and forests climb up the valley slopes,—visions which undulate according to the current of the stream and vary with the movement of the waters. Narcissus is wonderstruck as he looks;—but he cannot understand (for the one and the other are equipoised), whether it is his soul that guides the stream, or the stream that guides his soul.

The place where Narcissus is looking is the present. Out of the most distant future, things which are still only potential hurry towards existence; Narcissus sees

4

them, then they pass by; they flow away into the past. Soon it strikes him that everything is always the same. He wonders; he reflects. They are always the same forms that pass; the movement of the current alone differentiates them.—Why are there so many? or why are they the same?—It must be because they are imperfect, since they are always re-commencing . . . and all of them, he thinks, are striving and rushing towards a lost primaeval form, paradisial and crystalline.

Narcissus dreams of Paradise.

I

PARADISE was not large. Its every form, being perfect, blossomed only once; a single garden contained them all.—Whether it existed or did not exist, what does it matter to us? But if it existed, it was thus. Everything in it crystallised into a necessary flowering, and everything was perfectly what it ought to be.—Everything remained motionless, for nothing desired to be better than it was. A calm gravitation alone slowly operated the revolution of the whole.

And as no propulsion ceases in the Past or in the Future, Paradise had not come into being,—it had simply existed for ever.

Chaste Eden! Garden of Ideas! where forms, rhythmical and sure, revealed their number without effort; where everything was what it seemed to be; where proof was unnecessary.

Eden! where melodious breezes were wafted, undulating in pre-ordained curves; where the sky spread its azure over symmetrical lawns; where the birds were the colour of time and the butterflies on the flowers made providential harmonies; where the rose was rose-coloured because the green-fly settled on it for the very reason that it was green. Everything was as perfect as a number and scanned according to rule; concord emanated from the relationship of lines between themselves; over the whole garden brooded a constant symphony.

In the centre of Eden, Ygdrasil, the logarithmic tree,

plunged its vital roots in the soil and cast over the surrounding lawns the shadow of its foliage, where Night reigned alone. In the shade, propped against the tree-trunk, leant the book of Mystery—in which can be read the truth all must know. And the wind, blowing among the leaves of the tree, spelled out all day long, the necessary hieroglyphs.

Adam religiously listened. Single, still unsexed, he remained seated in the shade of the great tree. Man! Hypostasis of the Elohim! Mainstay of the Divinity! For his sake, by means of him, forms appear. Motionless and central in the midst of this fairyland, he watches it unrolling.

But spectator, perforce and always, of a spectacle in which he has no other part to play but that of an eternal watcher, he grows tired of it.—Everything is being performed for him, he knows it,—but he himself . . . himself he cannot see. Since that is so, what does all the rest matter to him? Ah! just to see himself!—Doubtless he is powerful, since it is he who creates and the whole world hangs upon his look,—but what does he know of his power as long as it remains unaffirmed?—By dint of gazing at them, he cannot distinguish himself from these things; not to know where one ends—not to know how far one reaches! For all the same it is slavery if one daren't risk the slightest gesture for fear of smashing up the whole harmony.—And then after all, so much the worse! this harmony with its constant perfection of the common chord exasperates me. A gesture! a little gesture, just to know,—a discord, what the deuce!—Hang it all! a little something unexpected!

Oh, if he could but snatch! snatch a twig of Ygdrasil with his spellbound fingers, and break it! . . .

He has done it.

. . . First of all an imperceptible fissure, a cry, a cry that lengthens out, swells, becomes exasperated, whistles strident and soon starts howling like a tempest. The tree Ygdrasil, stricken, totters and cracks; its leaves, shivering and contorted, through which the breezes used to play, are convulsed by the rising gale and carried away and afar,—towards the unknown space of a nocturnal sky and towards those hazardous regions where flee also the scattered pages, torn from the great sacred book, which is disintegrating now leaf by leaf.

Up to the sky there rises a mist of tears and clouds, falling in tears and rising again in clouds: time is born.

And Man, terror-stricken, self-duplicated hermaphrodite, wept with anguish and horror, feeling surge up within him, at the same time as a new sex, the anxious, uneasy desire for that other half, so like himself—that woman who has suddenly arisen so close to him, whom he embraces, whom he longs to re-possess—that woman who, in a blind effort to re-create out of herself the perfect being and then stop breeding, will nevertheless carry in her womb the unknown creature of a new race and soon push into existence another being, still incomplete and incapable of sufficing to himself.

Unhappy race, who will spread over this world of twilight and prayers! The memory of the lost Paradise will bring desolation to your raptures, that Paradise which you will constantly and everywhere search for—which prophets will come to tell you of—and poets—here they are!—who will piously gather up the torn pages of the immemorial Book in which was to be read the truth that must be known.

II

IF Narcissus were to turn round, he would see, I expect, some green sloping bank or other, the sky perhaps, the Tree, the Flower—something stable, in fact, and lasting, but whose reflection as it falls on the water is broken and variegated by the swift flight of the stream.

But when will this water cease its flowing, and, resigned at last to becoming a stagnant mirror, when will it repeat in an image of like purity—so like, indeed, that it will be confounded with the very lines themselves of those fateful forms—so as actually in fact to become them?

When then will time stay its flight and allow this flowing stream to rest? Forms—forms divine and perennial!—you, who are only awaiting rest in order to reappear, oh! when, in what darkness, in what silence, will you crystallise again?

Paradise has always to be remade; it is not in some *ultima Thule*. It dwells under appearances. All things retain virtually the intimate harmony of their essence, just as every salt contains in itself the pristine shape of its crystal. Let but a time of tacit darkness come, when the waters fall more impenetrably: then, in the unperturbed abysses, the secret archetypes will blossom . . .

Everything is striving after its lost form; it transpires, but sullied, awkward, and unselfsatisfied, for it must always be beginning again, crowded, hampered by the neighbouring forms which are striving too to show themselves—for merely to be, no longer suffices; proof of

one's existence must be shown,—and every one is in-
fatuated by pride. The passing hour throws everything
into confusion.

As the flight of time is caused only by the flight of
things, each thing clings and strains in order to slow
down this race and be able to make a better appearance.
There are periods then when things go more slowly,
when time rests—or so one thinks; and as noise ceases
with motion, all is silent. One waits; one understands that
the moment is tragic and that one must not stir.

"There was silence in Heaven", is the prelude of every
Apocalypse.—Yes, tragic periods when new eras begin,
when heaven and earth withdraw into themselves, when
the book with seven seals is about to open, when everything is about to become stationary in an eternal pos-
ture. . . . But then an importunate clamour arises; on
the chosen plains where one thinks time is coming to
an end (always a few greedy soldiers part garments among
them and cast lots upon a vesture), when the Holy Women
are tranced in ecstasy, and the veil is rent which will
reveal the secrets of the temple; when all creation contemplates Christ stiffening on the supreme cross, as he
speaks the last words, "All is now accomplished. . . ."

. . . But then, no! All has to begin again, begin again
eternally—because someone casting lots did not stop his
vain gesture, because a soldier wanted to win a garment,
because someone was not looking.

For it is always the same trespass, which always loses
Paradise once more: some person who thinks of himself
while the Passion is being ordained, some vain boon
companion, who refuses subordination.[1]

---

[1] Truths lie behind Forms—Symbols. Every phenomenon is the Symbol of a Truth. Its only duty is to manifest that Truth. Its only sin, to
prefer itself.

We live in order to manifest. The rules of morality and aesthetics

Inexhaustible church masses—high and low—every day in order to put Christ again in agony on the cross and the public kneeling in prayer . . . The public!—when it is the whole of humanity that should fall prostrate—then *one* mass would be sufficient.

If only we were able to be attentive and look . . .

are the same. Every work which does not manifest is useless and for that very reason, bad. Every man who does not manifest is useless and bad. (In raising ourselves a little higher, however, we should see that all men manifest; but this ought not to be recognised till later.)

Every representative of the Idea tends to prefer himself to the Idea that he manifests. To prefer oneself—there lies the error. The artist, the man of science ought not to prefer himself to the Truth he wishes to utter: that is his only moral law; nor, for that matter, prefer either the word or the phrase to the Idea which they are intended to express; I might almost say that in that lies the whole of aesthetics.

And I do not pretend that this theory is new; the doctrines of renunciation preach nothing else.

The moral question for the artist is not whether the Idea he manifests is more or less moral and useful for the greater number; the question is that he should manifest it well.—For all things ought to be manifested, even the most pernicious. "Woe unto him through whom the offence arises", but "Offences must arise."—The artist and the man who is really a man, who lives for something, must have made the sacrifice of himself beforehand. His whole life is nothing but a progression towards that.

And now, what to manifest?—That is to be learnt in silence.

(This note was written in 1890, in the same year as the treatise.)

III

THE Poet is one who looks. And what does he see? Paradise.

For Paradise is everywhere. Let us not believe in appearances. Appearances are imperfect; they stammer out the truths which they shroud; the Poet must understand at the slightest hint and then repeat these truths. Does the Man of Science do anything else? He too searches for the archetype of things and the laws of their succession; in fact he recomposes a world which is ideally simple and in which everything is ordered normally.

But the Man of Science searches for these primal forms by a slow and timid process of induction, making his way through innumerable examples; for he halts at the appearance, and in his desire for certainty, he will not allow himself to guess.

But the Poet, the Poet who knows that he creates, guesses through and by means of all things—and a single one suffices, symbol as it is, to enable him to reveal its archetype; he knows that its appearance is only a pretext, a covering which shrouds it and by which a profane eye is brought to a stop, but which shows us that Itself is there.[1]

The Poet, in his piety, contemplates; and in silence plunges profoundly into the heart of things,—and when he, the visionary, has caught sight of the Idea, the inward and harmonious Number of its Essence which sustains the imperfect form, he seizes it, and then, regardless

[1] Has my reader understood that I use the word symbol for every thing that *appears*?

of that transitory and temporal form which clothed it, he is able to restore to it an eternal form, its own veritable form, in fact, its fatal Form,—Paradisiac and crystalline.

For the work of art is a crystal—a portion of Paradise in which the Idea re-blossoms in its superior purity; where, as in the vanished Eden, a normal and necessary order has arranged all forms in a reciprocal and symmetrical interdependence, where pride of words does not supplant Thought,—where rhythmical and unambiguous sentences, which are still symbols, but symbols that are pure, where words become transparent and revealing.

Such works can crystallise only in silence; but there are silences sometimes even in the midst of crowds, when the artist, taking refuge, like Moses on Sinai, isolates himself, escapes from things and from Time and wraps himself in an atmosphere of light above the busy multitudes. In him, slowly, the Idea rests; then lucid and full-blown, spreads forth, outside of Time. And as it is outside of Time, Time has no power over it. Nay, more; one wonders whether Paradise itself outside of Time was perhaps never anywhere else—never anywhere but ideally.

Narcissus, meanwhile, gazes from the bank at that vision which an amorous desire transfigures; he dreams. Narcissus, solitary and puerile, falls in love with the fragile image; with longing for a caress, he bends down to the river in order to quench his thirst for love. He bends down and suddenly, lo and behold! the phantasmagoria disappears; he can see nothing on the river now but two lips stretched towards his own, two eyes, his own, looking at him. He understands that it is himself, that he is alone and that he is in love with his own face. Around him is an empty azure, which is broken through by his pale arms, stretching out with desire through the shattered apparition and plunging into an unknown element.

He raises himself then, a little; the face draws back. The surface of the water, as once before, is diapered with colours and the vision reappears. But Narcissus knows now that kisses are impossible; one must not desire an image; a movement made in order to possess it shatters it. He is alone.—What is he to do? Contemplate.

Grave and religious, he resumes the calm of his former attitude; he remains—an ever growing symbol—and, as he bends over the appearance of the World, he feels, vaguely re-absorbed within him, the passing generations of mankind.

This treatise is perhaps nothing very necessary. At first a few myths were sufficient. Then people wanted to explain; pride of the priest who wishes to reveal the mysteries, in order that he may be worshipped; or else a lively sympathy and the apostolic love that induces one to unveil, and thereby profane by showing them, the most secret treasures of the temple, because it causes suffering to admire alone and one wants others to worship with one.

THE LOVERS' ATTEMPT

or

A Treatise on Vain Desire

To Francis Jammes

> *Desire is like a brilliant flame, and
> what it has touched is turned to nothing
> but ashes—light dust which a breath
> of wind disperses—let us think then
> only of what is eternal.*
>
> CALDERON: *Life is a Dream.*

The first edition of *La Tentative Amoureuse* was published in 1893 in *La librairie de l'Art Indépéndant*.

Our books will not prove very truthful accounts of ourselves—but rather of our wistful desires, our longing for other lives eternally denied us, for all sorts of impossible acts. I am here setting down a dream which has been disturbing my thoughts too much and now insists on coming into existence. A desire for happiness this spring has worn me out; I longed for something more perfect to blossom in me. I longed to be happy as if there were nothing else for me to be; as if the past did not always triumph over us; as if life were not made of its habitual sadness, and to-morrow the necessary sequel of yesterday; as if my soul, no sooner freed from its dream, were not already returning to its customary pursuits.

And every book is no more than a postponed temptation.

NO no! Neither the importunate laws of men, nor fear, nor shame, nor self-respect, nor respect for my dreams, nor you, sad Death, nor dread of the hereafter —none of these will prevent me from clasping with all my strength what I desire; nothing—nothing but the pride of feeling still stronger than what I know to be so strong and conquering it. But the joy of such a lofty victory is not so sweet, not so delightful as yielding to you, desires, and being vanquished without a battle.

When spring came this year, I was tormented by its loveliness; and as my desires made solitude painful, I went out into the country early in the morning. All day long the sun shone down on to the plain; I walked along, dreaming of happiness. Doubtless, I thought, there must be other lands than these desolate fields where I am taking my soul to pasture. When shall I get rid of my gloomy thoughts and be able to walk in the sunshine all wholly joy; when, forgetful of yesterday and of so many useless religions, shall I clasp boldly, without fear or scruple, any happiness that may come? And that evening I dared not go in, imagining too well too many fresh discontents; I walked on to the woods, where already, of old, my sadness had so often strayed.—Night came and the moonlight. The woods fell silent and marvellous shadows filled them; the wind shivered; the night-birds awoke. I made my way into a deep glade, where the whiteness of the sand shining under my feet served me as a guide. Between the branches of the trees, which became more widely spaced when the wind stirred them, there were seen floating over the glade the intangible shape of the mist. And in the middle of the night, as dews dripped from the leaves, perfumes arose and the forest became lovesick. There were quiverings in the grass; every object seeking, finding, creating harmony, the larger flowers swayed, and the pollen, lighter than the mist, floated away in dust. A secret, swooning joy thrilled under the branches. I waited. The nocturnal birds wailed. Then all was silent; it was the hush before the dawn; joy became serene and my solitude an ecstasy under the admonitions of the pallid night-time.

Qualquiera ventio que sopla.
Light dust which a breath
of wind disperses.

I

DAWN came. Luke, laden with flowers, left the
woods still in nocturnal darkness. Shivering a little
with the morning freshness, he sat down on a bank on
the outskirts of the forest to wait for sunrise. Before
him stretched a dewy lawn, diapered with flowers and
with misty, shining water. Luke was expecting perfect
happiness, full of confidence, and thinking it would come
and settle like a flying swarm of bees and that everything
was already on its way towards him. Morning was quivering with boundless joy and spring coming to life in
answer to a call of smiles. Songs rang out and there
appeared a bevy of young girls.

Wild with joy, drenched with the wet grass, their hair
still in disorder after the night, they started picking flowers
together, holding up their skirts pannier-wise so that they
showed their bare dancing feet. Then, soon tired of their
dance, they ran down to the meadows below, and to the
spring, where they could wash, admire their looks and
get ready for the day's pleasures.

When they parted each of them forgot her companions.

Rachel came back by herself in a thoughtful mood;
she picked up the dropped flowers and stooped as though
to gather fresh ones, but in reality to avoid seeing Luke
draw near. She picked buttercups, salvia and daisies, and
every kind of field flower. Luke brought fox-gloves from
the glades and violet blue-bells. He was close to Rachel;
and now she was plaiting her flowers into a wreath.
Luke would have liked, but did not dare, to add his

own flowers to her garland; and suddenly throwing them at her feet:

"These are the dark-coloured flowers that grow in the woods", he said. "I picked them in the shade—for you—since it is you who have come; I have been looking all night. You are as lovely as this year's spring, and even younger than I am. I saw your bare feet this morning. You were with your companions and I didn't dare go up to you; but now you are here alone. Take my flowers and come with me, I beg; let us teach each other fresh pleasures."

Rachel smiled and listened; Luke having taken her hand, it was together that they went in.

The day passed in play and laughter. Luke went home by himself in the evening. Night came, but for him no sleep: often leaving his bed, which was too hot, he walked about his room, or leant out of the open window. He wished he was younger and far handsomer, thinking that between two beings, love had the splendour of their bodies. All night long Luke desired Rachel. In the morning, he made haste to go to her.

A path bordered by lilacs led to her house; then there was a garden full of roses, surrounded by a low hedge; as soon as he had come near, Luke heard Rachel singing. He stayed with her till evening, and then he went back to her again the next morning;—he returned every day; he set out as soon as he was awake; in the garden Rachel was expecting him with a smiling face.

Days passed; Luke did not dare; it was Rachel who first offered herself. One morning when he did not find her in the usual shady walk, Luke decided to go up to her room. Rachel was sitting on her bed, her hair undone, almost naked, with nothing on but a shawl, which had already nearly quite slipped off her shoulders; she was certainly waiting. Luke came in, blushed, smiled,—but when he saw her lovely slender limbs, he felt a frailty in them, and kneeling down before her, kissed her delicate feet, and then pulled back over her a width of her shawl.

Luke wanted love but was afraid of carnal possession as of a thing that had been spoiled. What an unhappy education we have had, making us imagine as full of sobs and grief, or as morose and lonely, that voluptuous pleasure which in reality is a glory and a calm delight. We shall no longer pray to God to uplift us to happiness. —And then, no! Luke was not that kind; for it is an absurd mania always to make the person one invents like oneself.—Luke then possessed this woman.

How shall I tell of their gladness now, save by describing nature around them, glad too, sharing their joy. Their thoughts were no longer of any account; their only occupation now was to be happy; their only questions were longings; their only answers satisfactions. They learnt the confidences of the flesh and every day their intimacy became more secret.

One evening when he was about to leave her as usual, "Why are you going?" she asked. "If it is to another love, very good. Go! I am not jealous. If not, stay with me; come, my bed invites you."

After that, he stayed every night.

The weather had become warmer, the nights so fine that they no longer shut their window; and so they slept in the moonlight; and as a rose-tree in full bloom had climbed up and grown round their casement, they had captured some of its branches; the scent of the roses mingled with that of the flowers in their room. Because of their love-making they went to sleep very late; their wakings were like those that follow drunkenness—very late and finding them still tired after the night. They washed in a spring of clear water which flowed through the garden, and Luke watched Rachel bathing naked under the trees.—Then they went for a walk.

They would often stay out till evening, sitting on the grass and doing nothing; they watched the sun go down; then, when at last the air grew cooler, they went slowly back to their home. The sea was not far off; at night when the tide was high, they could hear the faint sound of waves. Sometimes they would go down to the shore; the way lay through a narrow, winding valley with no stream in it; gorse and broom grew there and sand was blown about in it by the wind; then the beach lay open before them; no boats, no ships, though the sea was smooth. Almost opposite, in the distance, the curved coast seemed to form an island, and at that very spot they saw what looked like the gorgeous gates of a park; in the evening they shone as if they were made of gold. —Soon Rachel could find no more shells in the sand. The sight of the sea bored them.

Not far off too there was a village, but they went through it rarely because of its poverty. When it was raining, or when, out of idleness, they did not go even into the meadows, Rachel would lie down and beg Luke, sitting at her feet, to tell her a story: "Talk", she would say. "I am listening now; don't stop if I doze; tell me about gardens in spring time; you know what I mean, and those lofty terraces."

And Luke told her about the terraces, the rows of chestnut-trees, the gardens hanging over the plain:—in the morning, little girls would come to play there and dance in rings, and the sun was still so low over the plain that the trees cast no shadows.

A little later, older, sedater young girls came to walk among the flower-beds and make garlands—"like those you yourself used to wreathe, Rachel". About noon, couples too would come in—and the sun having risen above the trees, the opaque vault of branches seemed to make the alley cooler; the couples who walked in it spoke to each other only in whispers. A little later, when it was less dazzling, one began to see the plain over which Summer seemed to lie stretched like a carpet. Strollers leant their elbows on the balustrades and bent over them; groups of women sat down and wound up skeins of wool which others used for their work. Hours passed away. School-time being over, school-boys would come up; there were children who played at marbles. Evening fell; strollers came singly now; some, however, still drew together, talking of the day as if it was already over. The shadow of the terrace reached down on to the plain, and on the faraway horizon, in the unclouded sky, the moon shone very clear and pure. "One night I came to ramble on the deserted terrace. . . ." Luke stopped and looked at Rachel who had fallen asleep to the sound of his voice.

They took another walk, still longer; it was at the end of the spring. Having climbed the hill on which their house stood, they found half-way up on the opposite hill-side, a canal. A row of poplars bordered it; a path followed it along the slope, and then the ground continued to go downwards. When they had crossed the canal by a bridge, the sun which was burning made them walk along the water's edge. Heat came up from the valley in waves; the air quivered over the fields; a high road in the distance was powdered with dust whenever a cart passed by; they saw Summer stretched on the plain. The path, the trees, the canal followed the windings of the hill perseveringly; so they too followed the canal along the hillside; on the opposite side a small thicket came to an end. That was all. They walked along thus for a very long time; but as they saw it was going on indefinitely, when they had had enough of it, they went back home.

II

MADAME—this story is intended for you. You know that our melancholy loves went astray in the plains; and it was you who in other days complained that I found it so difficult to smile. This story is for you: I have tried to find in it what gifts love brings us; and if I have found nothing but tedium, it is my fault; you have disenchanted me with happiness.—How brief the joy in a book, how quickly told; how commonplace is a smile without vice and without melancholy! And then, of what interest to us is other people's love, the love that brings them happiness?—Well, so much the worse for them, Luke and Rachel loved each other; for the sake of my story's unity, they did, in fact, nothing else; the only tedium they knew was that of happiness.—Gathering flowers was their single monotonous occupation. They never brushed aside desire in order to pursue something more remote; they had little taste for the languors of hope deferred; they did not know the impulse that leads one to repel the very thing one longs to clasp—as we did, ah, Madame!—from fear of possession and love of pathos. They straightway plucked every flower they desired, without thinking that in the warmth of their hands it would fade too quickly. Happy those who are able to love with no pangs of conscience! They had indeed hardly felt its weight at all, for it is not so much love, not so much sin that weighs on one, as repentance. They had thus fallen into the habit of barely glancing at those actions of theirs that floated on the waters of the past; their own joy came to them from their ignorance of sadness; they remembered only the kisses and enjoyings that can be repeated. Then came a moment when their lives were really blended into one. It was the summer solstice; in the perfect blueness of the air, the tall branches above them moved with sovereign grace.

Summer! Summer! That word ought to be chanted like a canticle.—Five o'clock;—I got up (dawn is here) and went out into the country-side. If people knew what freshness of dew lay on the grass, the coolness of the water in which the morning will wash its shivering feet; if they knew the rays of light that shine on the fields, and the sun-struck dazzle of the plain; if they knew the welcome of smiles with which dawn greets those who come down to it in the fields,—they would not stay sleeping in bed, I suppose—but Luke and Rachel are weary with night-time kisses, and this amorous fatigue puts more smiles perhaps into their dreams than dawn has put into the fields.

One morning, however, they went out; they reached the same valley and the canal they had followed one day in spring; but as they skirted the hill instead of climbing it, they came to a place where the canal rejoined a wide river; the canal was used for towing; they crossed the water over a sluice and followed the tow-path, with the canal on their right and the river on their left. On the opposite shore there was a road too. And these five parallel highways in the narrow valley went on into the distance as far as they could see. Their walk that day was long but not interesting enough to talk about.

They wanted to revisit the shore and went down to it again by the glen; they sat down beside the sea. The waves of a recent storm had washed up on to the beach deep-sea shells, pieces of wreckage, fragments of torn sea-weed; the waves, still swollen by the storm, were deafening with their continuous clamour. And Rachel suddenly became anxious; she felt that Luke was beginning to think. A colder wind blew; a fit of shivering overtook them; they got up.—Luke walked on ahead, too quickly, rather theatrically; a beam lay there, battered and black, strange heaps of piles, a fragment of a boat, pieces of exotic wood . . . at this sight they both stopped. After that, Luke looked at the sea; Rachel, of necessity, by instinct, leant on Luke and rested her head on his shoulder, vaguely feeling in him a turmoil, a thirst for adventure. They remained standing. The sun was setting, far off, beyond the gulf, past the narrow channel where, between the promontories, the infinite line of the sea could be seen fading away in the distance.

And, while the sun was plunging downwards, at that moment, facing them, as though on an island, the palings of the strange park, in the light of the dying rays, began to glitter in an inexplicable and almost supernatural manner; at least so it appeared to them, from the fact that they said not a word to one another about it; every bar, made of steel rather than gold, seemed to shine inwardly, of itself or because of an extreme polish; the most curious thing was that it seemed as if one could see on to the other side of the paling, though one could not exactly tell what. Luke and Rachel, each of them, felt that the other did not dare speak of it.

On their way home, Rachel found lying on the sand a cuttlefish's egg, huge, black, resilient, and so queerly shaped that it seemed it must be intentional, so much so that they thought it must have some extreme importance especially for them, and tried to think out a reason for it.

The recollection of that day left them with a vague uneasiness, and as, in spite of themselves, they kept thinking of that park, shut off from them by the sea, so, attracted and curious as they were, and having, moreover, no boat to take them, they decided one morning to set out and following the coast line to walk until they reached it.

They rose before dawn and started on their way. It was grey and still cool; they walked like pilgrims, serious, silent, preoccupied, having in mind an object which was not themselves; and their slackened curiosity had left in them the feeling of a task to be accomplished.—But, Madame, do not let us talk of them too much, for here we are almost beginning to like them.—Ah well, it can't be helped! For once they walked without minding the heat of the day, guided by a single thought, for now it was no longer a desire. And Rachel did not complain of the shifting pebbles or of the yielding sand into which their footsteps sank; sometimes they walked along the shore, sometimes cut across the fields; once they followed the bank of a river upstream until they found a bridge,—then went down again,—then cut across country again.—Ah! here they are at last almost at the foot of the wall—the wall of the Park; and, the better to defend it from approach, the sea-water, having been led into a ditch lined with stones, washed the foot of the wall and seemed to end there; but the wall went on into the sea like a dyke, so that nothing could be seen on that side but a dull flinty promontory. They went on. The ditch came to an end. Then they walked along, following the wall. The sun was crushing; the road stretched on before them; it was the time of day when garden walls give no shade. They saw, almost hidden under the ivy, a little shut gate. The wall turned insensibly, and the sun, turning too as the day was closing, seemed to be following them. From over the wall branches drooped down, but without stirring. From inside the park there rose what seemed like a continual sound of laughter, but fountains often make the same sound as words. Suddenly they found themselves again facing the sea. Then a great sadness overcame them and they sat down for a little before starting on their way home. Facing them, as though coming from the other side, a promontory jutted into the sea, a continuation of the wall at the foot of which the sea broke in an impassable moat. And their sadness overwhelmed them, filled them, coming in on them at the same moment and at every point by the smallest fissure. Above all they were wearied out by their long walk and because it had proved in vain. The sun was disappearing now behind the park; they went on walking in the encroaching shadow of the wall; they almost thought there was some mystery in it. At moments they seemed to hear a noise like fingers tapping on a window pane, but as this noise stopped as soon as they stopped walking, they thought it must be caused by the resonance of their footsteps. Night had already fallen long before they reached home.

The next day, as they were taking their mid-day rest, "Tell me something of the summer dawn," said Rachel, "since my laziness keeps me here beside you."

Luke began: "It was Summer, but before day break; the birds had not begun to sing; the forest had barely awakened."

"Oh, not a forest!" said she, "a glade. Day is breaking, and if the birds are not yet singing, it is because the valley, where night is still lingering, is too deep; but light is already whitening the hill-tops."

"Towards those lighted hill-tops," Luke went on, "and towards the high plateau above, two knights were making their way after having followed the valley all night.

33

They were silent and serious, after having ridden so long in the dark, and the tall oaks of the glade spread their branches above them. Their horses climbed slowly up the straight steep road. As they climbed it grew brighter around them. On the plateau it was daylight.—On the plateau stretched another glade, wider, cutting across the first, at right angles and then following the crest of the hill. The two riders stopped. One of them said, 'Let us stop here, brother. Our call is not along the same road. My courage is sufficient and I have no need of yours to come to my aid. When one is enough, the other is useless.' And the other said, 'Farewell, brother.'

Then, turning their backs on one another, each went on his own way towards his own solitary conquests.

Then all the birds woke up. There were amorous pursuits under the leaves and insects danced in the air. The flight of bees could be heard, and on the lawns fresh flowers, ready to be robbed of their sweets, opened out. Delicious murmurs arose.

Further on where the ground ended, nothing was to be seen but leaves; lower down in the valley, now less filled with shadows, were the floating tops of trees; and lower still, a mist. Oh, how we should have stooped forward to watch the deer coming down to drink!"

"And the two knights?" asked Rachel.

"Oh, never mind them!" said Luke, "let's think of the glade. About mid-day there came there a gathering of young women; they walked hand in hand, like you and your companions; they were laughing; then came some men clothed in silk, with absurd golden trimmings; they all sat down and talked together.

The day went by; they fell silent and the shadows lengthened on the mossy ground; they got up and went to look at the sunset. The glade was gradually filled with restlessness and murmurings; everything was preparing to sleep;—then everything became silent; it was evening and the branches were swaying to and fro; the grey tree-trunks looked mysterious in the dusk; the song of a twilight bird arose. Then, as the night was beginning, two riders were to be seen, coming back; they rode towards each other, because that was their road, and their horses looked as though they had been through some great fatigue. They themselves were bowed down and graver than they had been in the morning because their task had been in vain. Having joined each other without a word, they went down the path again, which itself went down the hill, plunging into darkness beneath the branches."

"Why then are you going away, Luke?" said Rachel; "what is the use of setting out on a journey? Aren't you my whole life?"

"But you, Rachel," said Luke, "you are not the whole of mine. There are other things besides."

III

MADAME, this story is boring me. You know very well that if I have turned phrases, it was for other people and not for myself. I wanted to point out a relationship between the seasons and the soul; we had then to get on to Autumn. I don't like giving up whatever task it may be that I have undertaken.

Two souls meet one day and because they were gathering flowers, they both fancied they were alike. They took each other by the hand, meaning to continue their way together. But the persistence of the past separates them. Their hands fall apart and so, by virtue of the past, each one continues on his way alone. It is a necessary separation, for only a like past is able to make souls that are alike. For souls everything is continuous. There are some, as you know—as we know, Madame—who travel along parallel lines and will never be able to approach each other.—So Luke and Rachel parted; one single day, one single moment in Summer, their two lines mingled— one single point of contact—and now they are already looking elsewhere.

On the sand, seated beside the waves, Luke was looking at the sea, and Rachel at the land. They tried at moments to recapture the love that was unravelling, but it was pleasure without surprise; it was a thing that was exhausted and Luke was glad at the thought of leaving. Rachel no longer tried to keep him back.—When they went out together, they walked reflectively—I might almost say pensively—each looking ahead, instead of so often looking at the other. Luke no longer thought of

36

love, but their love had left in them, as it were, a memory of great sweetness, like the scent of beautiful faded flowers—all that was left of their garlands—but with no sadness, no sadness.

On certain days they walked along in this way, languorously and without speaking. The splendid colours taken by the autumn leaves and so beautifully reflected in water made them prefer the water of the stillest pools, and they walked slowly along their banks. The woods were glorious and sonorous; as the leaves fell, they disclosed the horizon. Luke dreamed of the immensity of life. I say that because I myself dream of it and I think he must have done so too.—Luke and Rachel bore me, Madame. What more can I tell you about them?

They made up their minds to revisit the park with the wonderful gates. They found, as they skirted the wall, that the little secret door, formerly so tightly shut, without bolts, was now open; they went in;—it was an abandoned park.

Nothing could picture the splendour of its paths. Autumn had strewn the lawns and some of the branches were broken; grass had grown over the ways, grass in flower, weeds of all sorts; they walked over it silently, beside red-berried bushes where robin-redbreasts were singing. I love the splendour of autumn.—There were stone benches, statues, and a stately house stood there, with closed shutters and barred doors. In the garden there still lingered the memory of revels; over-ripe fruit hung on the espaliers.—When evening fell they returned home.

"Tell me about Autumn", said Rachel.

"Autumn," said Luke, "ah! it is the whole entire forest, and the brown pool on its outskirts. The deer come down to it and the horn sounds 'Tally-ho! Tally-ho!' The hounds bay; the deer take to flight. Let us walk in the thick of the woods. The hunt is in pursuit; it has gone by;—did you see the palfreys? The sound of the horn has grown fainter, further away in the woods.—Let us go back now to the quiet pool, where the dusk is falling. . . ."

"Your story is absurd," said Rachel; "no one says 'palfreys' nowadays; and I don't like noise. Let's go to sleep."

Then Luke left her, for he wasn't sleepy.

It was soon after that that they parted; a parting without tears or smiles; quiet and natural; their story was done.

They turned their thoughts to other things.

AUTUMN is here, Madame; it is raining; the woods are dead and winter will soon be upon us. I am thinking of you; my soul is burning and at peace; I am sitting by the fire-side; near me are my books; I am alone thinking, listening.—Shall we re-knit, as of old, those loves of ours, so filled with beauty and mystery?—I am happy; I am alive; I have lofty thoughts.

I have finished telling you this story which we found so tedious; great tasks are calling us now. I know that on the sea, on the ocean of life, glorious shipwrecks are lying in wait,—and lost sailors, and undiscovered islands. —But we stay, poring over books, and our desires go off towards more assured actions. It is that, I know which makes us more joyful than other people.—Sometimes, nevertheless, wearied by too continuous study, I go down to the woods in the rain, to watch the autumn coming to an end.—And I know that on some evenings, after coming in from my walk, I have sat down by the fire, as though intoxicated by the joy of life, and indeed almost sobbing in the extremity of my joy, as I felt stirring in my mind the gravity of the works that were to be accomplished.—I will play my part! I will play my part! I am alive. Among all works, it is the great silent ones that we have loved. Poems! History! Drama! We will pore over life,—as you did, my sister, meditating and thoughtful. Now I am leaving, but think, think, of the joys of travel. . . .

And yet, I should have been glad—winter has come—to have prolonged this story together with you. We should have gone off alone together for a town in Holland: the streets would have been filled with snow; on the frozen canals the ice would have been well swept. You would have skated with me for a long time, as far as the country; we should have gone into the fields where we should have watched the snow forming; it stretches into the distance, infinitely white; the icy air is pleasant. —The night comes, but shining with the snow; we shall go in. Now you will be with me in the room beside the fire, with curtains drawn, and all our thoughts.

Then, sister, you would say to me:

"There is nothing for which it is worth while turning aside from our path; let us greet all things as we pass; but our end lies beyond them—so let us make no mistake; these things move on and depart; let our end be immovable—and we will move on to attain it. Ah! woe betide those foolish souls who mistake obstacles for ends. There are *no ends*; things are neither ends nor obstacles —no, not even obstacles; there is nothing to be done but to pass them. Our only end is God; we shall not lose sight of Him, for He is visible through all things. From now on it is towards Him that we shall walk; in a path which is splendid, *thanks to us alone*, with works of art on our right, and landscapes on our left, and the path we have to follow before us;—and from now on must we not make our souls fair and joyous? For it is our tears alone which make sorrows spring up before us."

And you, objects of our desire, you are like those perishable concretions which, as soon as our fingers touch them, leave behind them nothing but ashes.—*Qualquiera ventio que sopla.*

Arise, winds of my thought, you who will disperse these ashes.

Summer, 1893.
YPORT AND LA ROQUE.

EL HADJ

or

A Treatise on the False Prophet

> O thou messenger, proclaim what is sent down to thee from thy Lord! If thou do it not thou hast not delivered His message.
>
> *The Koran*, v, 71.

> What went ye out into the wilderness to see? A reed shaken with the wind?—But what went ye out for to see? A man clothed in soft raiment?—But what went ye out for to see? A prophet?—Yea, I say unto you, and more than a prophet.
>
> *Matthew*, xi, 7-9.

El Hadj first appeared in the second number of the *Centaure*, September, 1897.

NOW that the beloved minarets of our town, to which we have at last returned, are re-appearing beside the setting sun; now that the people, exhausted with fatigue and exhilarated with desire, are rushing towards it . . . Allah! is my task at an end? It is not my voice now that is guiding them.

Ah! may they shout for love this evening on the threshold of their homes, since there they will find rest once more! For me, I choose to linger on in the desert. I have sealed my lips upon my secret for days and nights; I have borne, unaided, the burden of my appalling falsehood; I have kept up my pretence to the very end; lest, seeking in vain the goal of our long wanderings and never finding it, my people should succumb to their miseries and no longer be able to continue on their way.

Now, I can speak! I am alone. But in my despair what shall be my cry?

For now I know that there are prophets who all day long hide from the flock they are guiding the anxiety, the bewilderment, alas! of their own souls, that they simulate their past fervour in order to dissemble that it is dead—that they sob when night comes and they find themselves alone—that they are but dimly lighted by the un-numbered stars and, perhaps, by the too distant Idea, in which, nevertheless, they have ceased to believe.

But you, Prince, you are really dead; I myself laid you in the shifting sands; the wind blew; the sands rolled away like the waves of a great river and who can tell now the place of your vagrant sepulchre?—Was it you who led your people to the desert? Or were you yourself led by some other? What did you find in the wilderness? There is nothing there. It was nothing, was it not, that you found in the wilderness? But you would have gone further still, if it had not been for death. Prince, it was I who brought the people back from the wilderness.

Of a surety, I did not at first think myself a prophet; I did not feel I had any such call. I was only El Hadj, a mere teller of tales in the public places, and I was taken along with them because I could sing songs. I was told I had on my back the sign with which God marks his apostles; but I was not aware of it; if I had been, I should not have left the town; the fear of God would have prevented me from following them. But could I have imagined my history? A prophet, I? It was only the fate of others that I foretold.

We started off in a serried troop, no one knew why or whither. They paid me to amuse them; so I joined them; I sang them love-songs in the tedium of their long march, and wept with them for the women we had not brought with us; and so I gained their affection. We advanced towards the desert. The Prince went before us, carried in his closed litter; not one of us could see him. At night he slept alone in his tent and not one of us went near him; his solitude was protected by slaves and mutes. By what means did he drag us after him? What mysterious tie bound us to him? It was as though his decisions were laid on us all without any intermediary. For no one transmitted any order from him; we had no chief but him, and he always kept silence. Or did he perhaps speak to his carriers? In any case his voice never reached our ears. So that we seemed to be following one who never appeared to be leading. But the strange thing was—and even then it surprised me—that our march seemed to be pre-ordained and our road already laid out before us, as though others had already traced it. We astonished nothing on our way, and in the towns we approached, provisions were so easily found, and we were so little wondered at, that it seemed as though the expectation of our passage had already preceded us. And yet it was clear enough that we were not one of those caravans of merchandise which pass and repass from town to town, and which it is customary to receive. We might rather have been taken for some warrior troop, if we had carried more arms—but even before our peaceful intentions had become obvious, and even from a distance, no one was alarmed.

As soon as we left the Prince's domains, for manners' sake, we no longer camped inside the towns but at the foot of their walls and facing East. When the town had oases round it, we no longer went in under the trees as soon as night came on. The chilliness of the air there was hurtful; we camped on the edge of the gardens and grew accustomed to seeing before us nothing but interminable spaces which stretched beyond the reaches of our souls.

Sometimes in these gardens, before the close of day, I would walk, in the company of our purveyors, to fetch provisions from the market places, where the salesmen would barely question us; and indeed we soon found it difficult to understand their language; it was still our own, but their pronunciation of it was too different. And what could we have told them? Only that we had come from a Southern capital, and that during our long march Northwards, we saw the country becoming more and more desert-like. Sometimes, more for the sake of our own people than for these foreigners, who barely understood me, or even for the small children who, when

our camp was not too far from their town, would follow
us and stay in the evening to sit, either in silence, or just
whispering, beside our brushwood fire, showing no more
astonishment at our travelling equipment, or at the rich
embroideries that hung from our dromedaries' necks,
than just enough to make sure of them with their finger-
tips—sometimes I would sing and go on singing late into
the night, till sleep overtook me:

The town we have left,
　　Is, was, rich, great and beautiful.
If we had not left it,
　　We should never have spoken its name,
For we knew of no others.
Now we shall call it Bab-el-Khour,
　　So that we may speak of it among ourselves,
And carry its renown with us
　　Through the lands we cross.
Our town is fairer
　　Than all the others we have seen.
There are cafés in them where there is talk
　　In the evening, and where beautiful women dance.
The women we have left
　　Weep for love as they await us.
Each of us has many wives,
　　And the least of them is still very beautiful.
Outside our town there are fields of wheat and corn;
　　The earth is rich with cereals.
Our Prince is powerful among all princes;
　　No one may approach him;
No one has ever seen his face.
　　Ah! blessed is the bride
Who will gaze upon his countenance!
　　What dowry will be rich enough for him?

46

What perfumes will scent her hair?
   Where is she awaiting the bridal festivities?
To that place we will go.
   She languishes in the tedium of waiting
Beside the pools of her vast gardens.
No one may see her but the Prince,
But on the wedding eve we shall taste
In abundance of the milk of palms
And of sweet wine.

Thus, when the others were there, I sang the praises of our town, out of vanity—and I foretold ourselves a gorgeous future, so as not to be despised. But at night, when everybody had left me, I no longer felt such self-assurance, and,

"Of a truth," I said, "our town is great and beautiful, the one we have left; but the journey since then has been long, and as for the rest, what do we know of it? No doubt we must follow the Prince; but till when? and till where? And with what object is he leading us? No doubt the Prince knows; but to whom should the Prince speak?"

And though they expected no answer to their wretched question,

"The Prince will speak," said I, "to me."

"How will you manage?" said they. "No one is allowed to approach him."

"We must have patience", said I. "He who walks all night may enjoy the shade in the day-time."

And myself, as I said it, was full of hope.

The next morning, while we were going on over the plain and the last shades were disappearing, I thought to myself: What is the use of my singing, if it is not for the Prince that I sing? To-night I will go close to his tent; everyone will be tired and asleep; the Prince, who has not toiled by day, cannot sleep much at night; he will hear me, and I shall sing so sweetly that he will want to hear me again. All day long it was of this that I thought; fervour upheld me during the march, and the longing I felt for the night that I was going to fill with my song made its coming seem slow.

When the night came:

"O night!" I sang—and all was silent in the camp. The Prince's tent, outside the camp, made an isolated promontory, and from this the vast desert stretched far away.

"O night!"—and I broke off my singing with pauses, as if the wind, by carrying it away, would make the Prince regret not hearing the whole of it. . . .

> "A tent in the desert!
> A felucca on the waters!

But of the sands, El Hadj, what am I to say?" . . . And I repeated my pilgrim's name, thinking, and so it turned out, that the Prince would remember it after-wards, and might summon me to his presence. Then, as at that moment the huge moon dissolved in silence, thrilled, as I watched it, by an agonising emotion, wonder filled me that, after the day's heat, the sands should still have kept enough light to give them such a gleaming appearance of azure; and I sang:

> "They are bluer than the waves of the sea.
> They were brighter than the sky . . ."

And suddenly, like someone lamenting, I cried:

"For how many days have you kept saying, that our country's hills are getting further and further away and that we no longer have anything to sustain our fidelity but memories that are too distant? Since then, what have we seen in the wilderness? The wilderness! El Hadj! What can you say of the wilderness? There is nothing there. Is it not true, tell me, that you have seen nothing in the wilderness?

I have seen rivers, great rivers, disappear wholly in the sand; they did not, I suppose, flow into it; it was slowly that they sank into it; they disappeared in it like hopes.—Sometimes they re-appeared again further on; I do not suppose they rose; they simply came out of the sand again in a purer, filtered stream of water; they re-appeared like hopes. Further on there was nothing but sand; we had no idea what became of them.—Rivers, great rivers, it was not you that we went forth to see.

> Tell us! what did you see in the plain?
> The huge caravan passed through it.
> What can it have seen on the sand?
> Whitened bones; emptied shells;
> Nothing but traces; traces; traces,
> Wiped out by the wind of the desert.
> The immense wind of the desert passed by.
> Ah! What went ye out for to see in the plain?
> Was it a reed tormented by the wind?
> But what went ye out for to see in the plain?
> Was it then nothing you went out to see? . . ."

When day came I was afraid I should be importuned by the others because of my singing; but they had not even heard it.

We went on through the desert.

When the next night came, I drew near again to the tent and when the crimson moon rose up over the desert:

"O night! great night!" . . . I cried; then I went on in a much lower voice:

"Like a boat on the waves, Prince, a tent is bearing you along. Whither is it bearing you?" And as that night I had brought my viol with me, from pause to pause I feigned with it an answer to my questions.

"In the sun, before us, have you not swooned long enough, dismal wilderness?

Desert! When the night comes, do you still never come to an end?

Oh! if only the wind would carry me away on its wings to the further shore of this incandescent sea!

Oh! may it be to that place where the blood-stained moon, shepherd of the sky, goes to bathe, before returning to her pasture.

Beside the pools of vast gardens, like the beloved on her wedding eve, she adorns herself; she gazes at herself in the waters.

Her lover awaits the wedding eve, Prince, beside the hidden springs."

Thus my words grew bolder, almost to the point of affirmation; and yet, and yet, what did I know? Was that prophecy? . . . And I went on singing in ever tenderer, ever more pathetic, or ever wearier accents:

"Prince, where will this journey end?

Will it be in the repose of death?

Doubtless there are other gardens in the North,

Under a gentle sky, where the palm-trees dwindle away.

What are you dreaming of? Prince, are you asleep? Prince! Shall I ever see you? So that I may answer any children or grandchildren there may be, on how many countless evenings, 'Yes, it was so,' when they ask me, 'El Hadj! El Hadj! What was it you were taken to see in the desert? Was it a Prince clad in sumptuous garments?'

Prince! my whole soul is sighing; my soul languishes in longing for you. . . ."

And little by little, in keeping with my words, I felt myself possessed with love for him, so that, when, on the third night, as soon as I began to sing, I saw him come out of his tent in the light of the sky, clad in sumptuous garments, but with his face veiled—and, as I was still asking and fearing to ask in vain: "Prince! what did you go forth to see in the desert?"—then, when in a voice more subtly soft than any song I had ever heard, his unhoped for answer came:—"A prophet—and more than a prophet—El Hadj! Good pilgrim, you! to-morrow you shall come into my tent", then, I turned silent and spent the night sobbing with love until the dawn came.

But the next morning the desert was covered with mirages; for some time past the oases had come to an end; at most, in certain places where water was stagnating, there rose a meagre wood of palm-trees, so enhanced by the mirage that in the distance it had the appearance of a marvellous oasis. And nothing I assure you—lofty towns, palm-trees, pools—nothing, Allah! was a more bitter disappointment to us than these mirages. Sometimes, from early dawn, we marched towards them, and then till evening, only to have the desolation of seeing them, at first slowly, grow distant, and then, in the fading of the sun, dissolve and disappear.—Thus from virtues to virtues we shall march in hope, El Hadj, until death, and sustain ourselves to the end by the visionary mirage of we know not what felicity—like a man, who in order to lull himself to sleep in it, might carefully prepare a dream for his irrevocable slumber.—O dead Prince! in your visionless slumber, are you still thirsting for spring waters?—O visions of Paradise! happy is he in whom only the blackness of death can blot you out! Allah! it is you alone who are veritable.—I know there are some who say that such things are not unreal, that their objects are elsewhere and that we shall end by finding them—objects whose floating appearance, detached by too much heat,—approaches us ever nearer, ever more deceitfully within reach of our grasp. But since we could not grasp it, Allah! why did you offer it to us?—And in the morning we were puzzled and disconcerted when the horizon looked ragged,—and even the past seemed to lose its inevitable certainty, so much, when we turned towards the sun, did everything appear to melt and turn almost fluid.—But what I wonder at now, what fills me with patience, is the thought, ah! poor people! how great was your confidence! it was that which gave rise to my compassion . . . For, indeed, how did they know what was expected of them? What did they themselves expect?—In order to continue their march, it was enough for them to believe in a goal and that the Prince at any rate, knew what it was, and was leading them towards it with confidence. With what docility they followed, knowing nothing; for of what the Prince told me I did not think I could reveal anything; and moreover, they would not have understood. And what certainty, moreover, had he himself of the future he spoke of? If now he believed in this wedding, was it not only since he had heard me sing of it? But then he spoke so sweetly, so credulously, so confidently of the child to be born of it, who would bear his name rejuvenated, the name which so far no one had ever heard and which would gain the hearts of the whole people. He spoke of it with such grave conviction, that, in spite of the past and by very reason of my want of comprehension, I myself believed it.

"El Hadj!" he used then to say to me urgently, "you must believe in me with all your strength; the future needs it in order to come to pass."

"Prince! thanks to the strength of my love, I have believed in you."

"Sing now, El Hadj, sing the gardens where my love is awaiting me, but do not speak to me of her."

So, thinking of the monoformity of palm trees, I said to myself that, in order to make the dweller in the desert dream, I must speak of the countless ramifications of Northern vegetation, and of the variety of the tree-trunks; and I sang the depth of the forests, the ravines, the odour of leaves and moss, the mists of morning and of evening, the coolness of the night, the pleasantness of morning, the delicious moisture of the meadows. The Prince listened to me slowly. I spoke of the easier toil, the sweeter pleasures; the brighter azure, the cooler air, the less burning nights.

"Shall we soon be there?" he asked.

"We shall be there soon", I answered.

"Go on singing, beloved El Hadj!"

"Over there," I sang, "the running waters are no longer salt. Ah! how delicious the icy pebbles of the rivers will feel to our feet . . ."

Half the night went by in singing.

I do not know whether my singing gave the Prince confidence, but I myself was extraordinarily encouraged by it. What I sang came into being; after singing of it I believed in it. In the presence of the people I usually wrapped myself in silence; it was enough for them to believe that the Prince was guiding them. And when I spoke, it was to say:

"The Prince is your leader; he knows where it pleases him to go. But what can I say about that? What am I myself in his eyes? In your eyes, it is true, I am a prophet; in the Prince's eyes, a servant." And I fell prostrate with my face turned towards his tent in sign of submission.

Meanwhile every afternoon became more overpoweringly hot. When the mirages did not form, there was absolutely nothing to be seen before one but the tawny sands of the desert, occasionally reaching the height of sand-hills. In order to occupy the time, I invented stricter observances and singular privations. We had brought hardly any women with us in our camp, but I fixed times for allowing them to be touched; yet the hearts of the people were not overflowing with love for the Prince as was mine. In their presence I behaved with haughtiness, and in order to prevent them from asking questions, I said nothing that was not incoherent: to the submissive, I made promises of rewards, to the rebellious threats of punishment. Then I went back to be near the tent into which the Prince allowed me to enter only in the evening, and until evening came, I felt my confidence melting away, though once near the Prince, it once more revived. But, I know not by what means, when I had weakened during the day-time, in the evening, the Prince knew it.

"El Hadj!" he would say then, in an ever feebler voice, "it is on your faith that I lean; it is from your belief in me that I draw the certainty of my life."

I did not understand at the time, but, after each day of misgiving, in the evening I found him still a little feebler. Alas! that is why each morning my faith too awoke ever feebler; on the other hand, while I was regaining confidence all through the long night I spent beside him, he himself was in no way strengthened by it.

"El Hadj!" he would say then, "doubting prophet! How slight is your love! Is it worth while that I should live on it?"

"Oh!" I would reply, "I love you, Prince, as much as it is possible for me to love you. It is at noon that everything falters; at night as I sit beside you, I am consumed with fervour. Why do I not spend the whole day in your tent? We should console each other during the long hours; in the day-time too I love you; I long for the night and weep that you do not show yourself to me. Why do you not let us know you better? It is only you I desire to know. Ah! if I could see your face, Prince, what strength would be mine!" Then the Prince took my hand in his, and it gave me an agony of anxiety . . . My tenderness was increased, but my confidence was heart-stricken— so burning with fever was his hand.

On the following day, between the long marches, near the tent which was already pitched, in the hopes that he would hear me, I went on with my singing:

> My tent sails over the desert
> As over a fiery sea.
> Canvas doors, let the wind blow you open!
> Doors of my tent, you are riddled with light.
> Blow open, O canvas doors,
> And let in my desire.

But the wind barely did more than make the canvas flap like the sail of a ship. The Prince slept all day and did not hear my singing. Then I went on in more of a murmur:

> My sweet friend is asleep in his tent.
> I watch so that he may sleep.
> When I am alone it is because I await my friend.
> It is only at night that I go to him.
> This is now the hour of the fires of noon;
> The whole earth is perishing of thirst and fear and longing;

The hour when the will of brave men shakes with terror,
When the mind of wise men is bewildered,
When the virtue of the pure is adulterated,
For thirst is the desire for love
And love is the thirst for contact,
   And all that is not fire
Grows pale in this ardour.

There are some who, at the coming of evening, fail to
    recover their courage,
So wearied are they by the fierceness of the heat;
There are some who, throughout the desert,
Have searched in vain for their straying thoughts.

For my friend's sake,
I await without fear the gentle night.
When night comes, my friend wakens;
I go to him; we spend long hours consoling each other.
He leads my eyes to wander in the gardens of the stars.
I speak to him of the great trees of the North,
And of the chilly pools where the moon,
Shepherd of the sky, goes to bathe like a bride;
He explains to me that only perishable things
Have invented the only possible words
And that those things which are not doomed to perish
Are for ever silent, for they have all time in which to
    speak—
And their eternity speaks for them.

    Hardly understanding why, I was frightened by these strange words of the Prince's which I repeated in my song, singing thus because of the very silence of the desert.

    That night, when I saw him again in the dimly lighted tent, he was weary.

"Prince," I said, "I must have a token of the amity that unites us two—a token which, in default of you, I may possess and be able to look at in the course of the day."

"What!" said he, "don't you understand, El Hadj, that you yourself are the token of the amity that binds the people and me? And that between you and me no sign is possible, since from you I am not hidden. What else do you want other than myself? You care for me, I know, but you do not care enough for your people; and yet all they know of me is yourself: it is with your features that I appear to them, and with your voice that I speak to them. You do not speak to them enough, so how do you expect them to love me?"

Then, almost sadly, I thought, and in a voice that was a little changed, he added, "Yes, I will show you my face, but the sight of it will not bring satisfaction to your love". And getting out of bed and tottering like the weakest of invalids, he raised the canvas of the tent and, under the paleness of the Heavens uncovered the paleness of his own face. He was beautiful with an unearthly beauty and seemed to be of another race than ours, but so unutterably pale and with an expression so weary that lo! my faith began to disappear, and, in its stead, I felt myself invaded by a wholly human love. And I stood before him, motionless and speechless, until, at last, falling at his feet . . . I clasped his frail knees with my arms, and then thought I should faint away with tenderness, doubt, and desolation, as I felt, laid upon my all too burning forehead, the clammy warmth of his hand.

It was the next day, in the evening, after a long march, and after crossing an ultimate sandhill, that there appeared, as in answer to our gasping, breathless desire, the gentle azure plain of a lake or sea. Then, the delirious outcries of the foremost among the followers having made the others hasten onwards, there arose among the whole people an indescribable stir; as if the sight of so near a coolness afforded them hope enough to satisfy their longing and already sufficed for one evening to quench their thirst; prostrate, as though in prayer, they called to the waters, and their thirst, sensing it would so soon be slaked, turned to rapture. Songs arose and cries, as of a grateful and gratified sensuality; others among them danced. Not one of them had any further thought of going on; as if promises could suffice instead of satis-factions; as if thirst had ever been quenched by salt water, love by visions or hope by illusions. The shore was barely a league distant from us, but after our im-mense fatigue, this immense joy was shattering. No doubt, in his close-curtained bed, which was always at the head of the march, the Prince heard his people's delirious shouts. The porters, on the downward slope of the sandhill, stopped, and the royal tent was pitched. The sun was setting in a gathering cloud of mist or dust, which was reddened by its slanting rays; the horizon beyond the sea melted away in golden love-liness; for a moment, the waters, in a reflection of the heavens, seemed incandescent, then, suddenly, as the great disc disappeared, night came, total and hermetic.

I knew that sometimes the tides spread widely over stretches of flat ground and that the beaches of unknown seas are often dangerous; so that I was glad that we had stopped where we were still far off from the sea and high up on the hill-side. The camp was pitched; the evening lights shone brightly. The Prince's tent, hardly lighted at all, stood out in front of the camp like an

isolated promontory; night seemed filled with the sea.
—I drew near the Prince's tent.

He was standing, having raised the tent door and was
looking out; his face was unveiled and his eyes were
scrutinising the darkness. When he saw me, "I cannot
see the sea", he said, "El Hadj!"

He spoke mysteriously; hearing him pronounce my
name, I felt an almost lover-like tenderness.

"Because the night is dark", I answered. "The moon
will soon be rising."

"I cannot hear the sea, El Hadj."

"Oh, Prince, because it is very calm, and we are too
far off."

"El Hadj!" he went on slowly, "it is on the other side
of these waters that my wedding has been made ready
and that our coming is awaited with growing expectation. El Hadj, in spite of the dark, through the dark,
where no one can see you, you must go down to the
sea; the moon will rise when you reach the shore; look
if you can see the other side; if the trees can be distin-
guished—those great trees of which you sing. Go, my
El Hadj! Beloved El Hadj! Go quickly and then come
back to me directly."

I started at once; I set out in spite of my fatigue; I went
down the slope of the sand-hills and was soon wrapped
in a heavy cloak of darkness. Looking back towards the
camp, I saw no light coming from it; it was hidden by
an almost opaque fog, into which I plunged still further
as I went down towards the shore. I trusted that the
moon would light me back. I was tired, so tired that
I forgot what it was I hoped for. I was astonished, I
remember, at the faint, almost sickly odour of the air;
the moisture it was charged with had not, as was to be
expected, the sea's rough and briny saltness, but brought

to mind rather the exhalations of marshlands. And suddenly, in front of me, as I walked, the mist shivered, quivered, silvered, opened, and, like a shepherd watching his folds, the moon gravely took up her watch in the sky.

She floated above a plain of inconceivable stillness. I was on the shore of a far-stretched mystery, where not a ripple stirred but over which laughed and shone the fair and indefinitely magnified image of the moon. The land came to an end insensibly; the flatness of the sand was simply prolonged into something else, which reflected the solitude, but which I realised was not water. I went on; I went in; it was like some half-created matter, neither quite solid nor quite liquid, responsive to my foot and not altogether firm, but, as it were, imperfectly solidified. On my left a spur of sand jutted out, on and on, a narrow promontory, on which was a growth of miserable reeds. I walked on to it . . . then, it became, no, neither land nor water . . . a kind of mud, of slush, covered by a thin crust of salt and faintly silvered by the moon. I tried to go on further; the fragile crust broke through; I sank into a loathsome soft mud. Catching hold of the reeds, crawling face downwards on my knees, I went back to rest on the sand. There I sat down; I looked about me; my astonishment was so great at the sight of this desolate sea and this salt-covered morass in which the weight of my body had dinted a hole—that I was conscious of nothing else, not even of my own utter hopelessness. Overcome with weariness and stupor, I looked at the moon, smiling serenely, as it were, over the pale expanse beneath her, and shedding her brightness on the dismal, unfathomable plain, more dismal even than the desert itself.

And now the moon was higher still in the sky, shining

more brightly on the horizon, and showing on the other side of the sea another not very distant shore; and there seemed to be great trees bending on it. . . . But the sand on which I was sitting began to give way beneath me; I was obliged to leave the promontory and go back to the slope where the sea ended. There I lay down on the ground and there I felt my solitude and the surrounding immensity so absolute . . . and this sea, I said to myself, for all its narrowness, will not be any easier to cross . . . that all my virtue suddenly abandoned me; it did not take to flight, I suppose; it just disappeared like water disappearing in the sand; it vanished completely. I suddenly felt without courage, like someone whose faith has completely deserted him. A desolation without tears, even vaster and as dismal as the desert, seemed to flow in on me, spread and overwhelm me.

I was too tired to go back at once to the tents, and what could I have said to the Prince? And yet, in spite of everything, the night was so bright, so pure, so delightful, that my mind, discomposed as it was, took pleasure in it. Nevertheless, intoxicated by the night that precedes the dawn, and afraid of meeting persons who had already left the camp and gone down to the sea, and who, having realised its falseness, would harrass me in my grief with their foolish lamentations, as soon as I saw the night sink languishing at last on the sandhills, where whiteness was dawning, I went on my way back to the tents.

Refulgence glimmering from all quarters of the sky! O! shaking knees, outstretched hands! anxious clinging to the shade! Prophet! Yes, I am he.—Prince! it was given to me to speak to your people when you could say no more. Ah! long marches in the desert; expectation of one knows not what; aching knees; increasing thirst; flight of uneventful hours; weary nights; dreary days;

oases fading away in the evening light. Trees of the North; groves vaguely longed for; ah! promontories! promontories thrust forth towards the sky, where one walks on and on; and then one's strength gives way . . . White moonshine on the tents! end of the night; refulgence glimmering from all quarters of the sky . . . Then O raised canvas door! mysterious tent into which I entered! Canvas door dropped down again, as silence drops down upon a secret; couch over which I leant, lighted by an expiring flame; couch horribly hollowed and looking empty, where the Prince lay lifeless.

Prince, you were wrong; I hate you. For I was not born to be a prophet; it was your death that made me one; it was because you no longer spoke that I was obliged myself to speak to the people. . . . Peoples forsaken in the desert, it is only for you that I weep.—You, departed Prince, do I really hate you? Who knows? . . . But I am languishing with emptiness, with weariness, with hunger, because I loved you so; and the remembrance of those nights of yours makes my solitude more desolate.

I had not loved the people before then, but from that time on I pitied them. Did *you* love them? What was the good of your leading them so far away from the towns? For the sound of your wedding feast never reached us. We did not hear the songs of flutes and cymbals. My ears are expectant to the utmost. Where can that wedding have been celebrated that the rumours of it have already faded? Prince, I will tell no one. No one knows that it is in death that they have turned so silent.

Prince, I have had to deceive the people, because you had already deceived them and because I knew and had taken pity on your falsehood. Prince, I prolonged your wretchedness beyond and further than your death. I retraced your whole journey backwards. You led the people into the desert; I led them back to the town where they could have their fill of food and drink as a recompense for the days of stretches of hunger which, indolent shepherd that you were, you made our only pasture in the long stretches of arid sands.

The early dawn was quivering; it was the hour when on other days I used to leave the Prince. I came out of his tent with dry eyes and composed face. No one so far had gone down to the shore. I wanted to prepare their coming despair; make them look upon their fright-ful disappointment when they got down to the sea as a punishment; to invent some kind of crime; offer the people, as it were, the opportunity of committing a sin which would account for their punishment—so that they might consider their fate as more or less deserved and therefore, if not less grieved by it, at any rate, feel sub-mission and fear towards me. I, who had been led by love alone, I could only lead them by fear. And so, not-withstanding the impatience of their thirst, or rather, because of it, I said:

"The Prince wishes to put your fidelity to the test. He does not intend to go down to this longed for shore after any one of you. 'Am I not the first among them?' he says. 'Ought I not to be the first to step into this sea, to bathe in it, to drink of it? Woe then to him who goes down to it before me; such a one would be cruelly punished for this outrage, and not he alone. If indeed, there were only one of you to commit this sin, you would all undergo the penalty of his fault. For my wrath will exceed all expectation and will seem greater than the sin. I require,' he said to me, 'the people to fear me and I hope for their absolute submission; now this sin, even if committed by a single one of you, would be a sign to me of an absolute lack of submission. But listen; I have no intention of going down to the sea, either to-day or to-morrow, but only on the morning after the second day; and that is where the test will lie; in spite of your thirst, you must wait. Before approaching the water, you must raise an altar to God as an act of grace, and in order to make sacrifices on it. This is how you will spend your two days. You must build this altar a very short distance away from the shore, without minding whether it is on shifting sand or not. You will find enough gypsum to make plaster and, at the foot of the sand-hills, blocks of conglutinated sand. Underneath the altar must be dug out, as it were a cellar. Start at once. I want you all to work at it. I am impatient to begin sacrificing.'"

During the tedious waiting of those two days, and notwithstanding the constraint put on them, the work went on quickly. I do not know whether perhaps one of them had not already disobeyed my order secretly. It did not matter. If they were all to obey, the sea would not be any different. It would always be possible to imagine that there had been one sinner for whom the others were suffering. They could not all know what each single one of them might have done.

During the tedious waiting of those two days, the sea was of an azure blue . . . The other shore was vaguely visible, crowned with mirages, which varied with the course of the hours. I stayed beside the Prince's tent, so as to make it easier for them to transgress. At night, I went down as far as the shore, knowing it to be treacherous. I sat down near the edge, wholly possessed by gazing. The moon rose fuller than on the night before; as I was less astonished, I was better able to contemplate it. It seemed that the silence, there, was actual and real, and that it was my worship. For I had not known before that a night could be so beautiful; and I felt in myself, deeper than I had thought any depth could be found in me, another love, a thousand times more fervent, gentler, more restful than the love I had felt for the Prince, and to which I thought this immense calm was a response.

So that, more peaceful still, on this third night—when the moon came to lighten my steps down to the foreshore; when, wearied pilgrim that I was, like a robber in the night, I had carried, had dragged the Prince by a fold of his cloak which had half covered his face, that Prince, whom I might have seen now in all his nakedness, was no more than a corpse and not worth thinking of; when I had placed him under the narrow altar where, on the morrow, the people, in derisory penitence, would make their sacrifice—when I had stretched him in the narrow hollow I had had dug for that purpose . . . then, at last, in the desolation of deliverance from the love of my soul, alone in the night, I was able to cry my joy aloud and, flinging from me my dead past, give vent to my hope in song. Before then, I had not suspected how tired I was of this pilgrimage, but that evening as I went down to the shore for the last time, it was without fear that I looked upon the sea, which after all was only to be feared by one who might think he would have to cross it. And I saw it then as something so beautiful, that I felt my yesterday's faith very slowly shifting its ground; my adoration was as intense as ever, but now that the Prince was dead, it was diffused, spreading invincibly to the furthest limits of the infinite desert; and because my soul, possessed of deeper gravity, was imbued with majesty, I thought it was happiness.

Now that I think that this is an impossibility, I doubt

whether I ever really attained happiness. I remember I wanted to sing, but I was unable to, since there was no longer anyone to sing to, so I said over and over again to myself alone, without understanding what I said, "Prince! Who then is dead? How is it I am so much alive?"

Joy? Perhaps. I did not then understand how great at that very moment was his triumph; for he was dead for me alone, for me, who was precisely the only one to love him. His emptied litter must always lead on at the head of the people. I must incessantly bear witness that I had seen him, and I could no longer speak save to transmit his words. I did not at first realise what a burden the reality of my falsehood put upon me, and that the dead Prince survived in my falsehood. For my love was fanned by constantly having to imagine him. I knew nothing of him but that he was dead, I could not imagine him anything but alive. Sometimes at night, in his tent, I slept—alone now. And my dreamless sleep seemed to me like a representation of his death; but sometimes the fact that other people were near his tent made me pretend that I was singing to him; then I remembered our nights together and grieved at the recollection of his face. My grief persisted desperately in simulating his presence to the last. Every day his meals were brought to him as to a living person; every thing I did in order to represent him to others helped me to realise better that he was gone. The more I felt he should have been there, the more I knew that he was not.

And from that day on, I was possessed by the thought, as wearing and as powerful as a desire, that I shall indeed enjoy the happiness of my soul, even now awaiting me, but only when I have been freed from the people and from love once and for all.

And now the people have left me; they have at last
returned to their town. I have brought them back from
the desert. They never loved me because I spoke my
prophecies harshly, afraid as I was of becoming too piti-
ful; neither did they love the Prince, for I put no words
into his mouth that were not rough. I could not speak
of love for him, since it would have been for a falsehood.
I had to impose him on them to the very end; avoid any
authorisation of weakness on my part. Since I had no
power, was it not my duty to simulate? But I know now
that if prophets there are, it is because they have lost
their God. For if He did not keep silence, where would
be the use of our words?

No doubt too I have performed false miracles; I have
made water gush forth from rocks; I have turned false
springs to sweet and when there came a flight of quails,
I said it was because I had prayed. When Boubaker re-
volted, I do not know how I managed to quell the rebel-
lion, unless it was that I acted in desperation. I used
threats. After that no one had any doubt of my power;
it was only I myself who failed to be convinced of it.

My shepherd's task is at an end; my soul is at last
delivered. What now can I cry aloud for joy? There are
no songs now that I can sing. No longer now, in the
evenings, flooded with love, can I call aloud my verses
in the open places of the town; no longer make the
children dance. No longer now can I ever have known
anything but the town, never have traversed the desert.
—Now, El Hadj, what am I to do? That the Prince is
dead—do I really know it? I remember the wedding
feast that awaits him, as if he were in no way dead. . . .

Here, here, inside the palace of the Town, I know that
there is growing up a young brother of the Prince's. Is

he waiting for my voice to guide him? And am I to start again with him and another troop of followers, a fresh story, which I shall recognise step by step? Or, like those unhappy creatures, filled with woe, and fed upon bitter ashes, shall I depart into the solitude alone?—like those who, hiding their secret, wander about grave-yards, seeking for rest in desert places, and never finding it.

PHILOCTETES

or

A Treatise of Three Ethics

To Marcel Drouin

Philoctetes was not written for the stage. It is an essay on three differing ethics. I have included it with the other treatises in this book, the better to show that it has no theatrical intentions. (Note by André Gide.) *Philoctetes* first appeared in the *Revue Blanche*, 1st December, 1898, having previously been announced under the title of *Traité de l'Immonde Blessure*. A year later it was published by the *Mercure de France*.

ACT I

A grey lowering sky over a stretch of ice and snow.

(*Ulysses and Neoptolemus*)

NEOPTOLEMUS

Ulysses, everything is ready. The boat is moored. I have chosen a place where the water is deep and sheltered from the North, for fear the sea should be frozen by the wind. And though this island is so cold that it seems to be inhabited only by the birds of the cliffs, I have fastened our boat where no passer-by on the coast could see it.

My soul too is ready; my soul is ready for the sacrifice. Speak now, Ulysses; everything is ready. For fourteen days, bending over the oars or the helm, you have spoken only the brutal words of command needed to preserve us from the waves; your obstinate silence soon put a stop to my questions. I understood that a great sadness was weighing on your beloved soul because you were leading me to my death. And I kept silence too, feeling that all words were too quickly carried away, by the winds and over the sea's immensity. I waited. I saw the fair Skyrian beach, where my father had fought, vanishing behind us, behind the sea's horizon: then the golden-sanded or rocky islands, which I loved because I thought they were like Pylos; thirteen times I saw the sun drop into the sea; every morning it rose again out of the waters paler and paler and mounted less high and more slowly, until at last on the fourteenth morning we waited for it in vain; and since then we have been living, so to speak, outside of night and day. There was ice floating on the sea; and unable as I was to sleep because of the constant pale glimmer of the sky, the only words of yours that I heard were to give warning of the icebergs, from which the stroke of an oar was needed to save us. Now speak, Ulysses! I have made ready my soul; and unlike the rams of Bacchus which are led to the sacrifice covered with festive ornaments, but like Iphigeneia, advancing to the altar, simple, seemly and unadorned. No doubt, I should have wished, like her, dying for my country without a complaint, to die at home among the Greeks, in a land of sunshine, and to show by my acceptation of death all my respect for the gods and all the beauty of my soul; my soul is valiant but has never known as yet what it is to fight. It is hard to die without glory. Yet, O ye gods! I am without bitterness, having slowly left all things behind me, men, sunny beaches . . . and now that we have reached this inhospitable island, without a tree, without a ray of light, where all greenery is covered with snow, where all things are frozen, where the sky is so white, so grey, that it looks like another plain of snow spread above our heads, far, far from everything . . . so that it seem as though death were already here, and as though my mind, becoming hourly colder and purer, all passion spent, nothing is left now but for my body too to die.

At least, Ulysses, tell me whether this mysterious Zeus, satisfied by the shedding of my faithful blood, will grant the Greeks victory; at least, Ulysses, you will tell them, won't you, that that is why I go to my death without fear. . . . You will tell them. . . .

ULYSSES

Child, you are not going to die. Don't smile. I will speak to you now. Listen to me without interrupting. Would that the gods might be satisfied with the sacrifice of one of us two! What we have come to do here, Neoptolemus, is not so easy as dying. . . .

This island, which you take to be deserted, is not so at all. A Greek lives on it; his name is Philoctetes and your father loved him. Long ago he set sail with us in the fleet that bore us so hopefully and proudly from Greece to Asia; he was the friend of Hercules and one among our nobles; if you had not lived for so long at such a distance from our camp, you would already know his story. Who did not then admire his courage? Who, later on, did not call it rashness? It was by this that he was overborne when our oars were held up by an unknown island. The look of the shore was strange; bad omens had damped our courage. The gods' orders, said Calchas, being that we should make a sacrifice on this island, each one of us waited for someone else to go ashore; it was then that Philoctetes offered himself with a smile. On the beach a treacherous serpent bit him. He was still smiling when, on coming aboard again, he showed us a little sore place just above his foot. It got worse. Philoctetes soon stopped smiling. His face grew pale, then his anxious eyes filled with an anguished astonishment. After a few days his foot became swollen and heavy; and he, who never before had been heard to complain, began to groan lamentably. At first everyone surrounded him with attentions and tried to comfort and distract him; nothing was any good; what was wanted was a cure; and when it became clear that Machaon's art had no effect on his injury and as his cries too threatened

to affect our spirits, when our boat approached another
island, this one, we left him on it, alone with his bow and
arrows, which are our concern to-day.

NEOPTOLEMUS

What! alone! You left him, Ulysses?

ULYSSES

Oh, if he had been going to die, we might have kept
him some time longer, I think. But no. His injury is
not mortal.

NEOPTOLEMUS

Then what?

ULYSSES

Then should we have esteemed the army's valour as
less important than the distress, the lamentations of a
single man? It's obvious enough you didn't hear him!

NEOPTOLEMUS

Were his cries so dreadful then?

ULYSSES

No, not dreadful; plaintive; drenching our souls with
pity.

NEOPTOLEMUS

Couldn't someone at least have stayed with him, to
look after him? Ill and alone, what can he do?

ULYSSES

He has his bow.

74

NEOPTOLEMUS

His bow?

ULYSSES

Yes; Hercules' bow. And then, I must tell you, my boy, that his diseased foot gave out over the whole ship the most intolerable stench.

NEOPTOLEMUS

Ah?

ULYSSES

Yes. And then he was entirely taken up by his ailment, incapable from henceforth of any further devotion to Greece. . . .

NEOPTOLEMUS

It couldn't be helped, no doubt. But we then, Ulysses, we have come . . .

ULYSSES

Listen, Neoptolemus; you know what a length of years we spent before ill-fated Troy, at what expense of blood, and virtue and patience and courage; how many homes have been deserted, how many fatherlands forsaken . . . Nothing of all that has sufficed. The gods at last declared, through the priest Calchas, that only Hercules' bow and arrows, by a supreme virtue, would bring victory to Greece. So, we two having set forth—thanks be to the lot that was cast in our favour!—, it seems now that on this distant island, all passion spent, our lofty destinies will be at last accomplished and our souls here

in the most total abnegation will attain at last the utter-
most perfection of virtue.

NEOPTOLEMUS

Have you done, Ulysses? And now, having made such
a good speech, what is it you intend to do? For my mind
still refuses to grasp your meaning. Tell me! Why have
we come here?

ULYSSES

To take away Hercules' bow. Haven't you grasped
that?

NEOPTOLEMUS

Is that your intention, Ulysses?

ULYSSES

Not mine, but that which the gods have given me.

NEOPTOLEMUS

Philoctetes will never give it up to us.

ULYSSES

No. We shall have to get it by cunning.

NEOPTOLEMUS

Ulysses, I hate you. My father taught me never to
make use of cunning.

ULYSSES

Cunning is stronger than force. Your father is dead,
Neoptolemus. I am still alive.

NEOPTOLEMUS

And didn't you say it was better to die?

ULYSSES

Not that it was better, but that it was easier to die.
Nothing is too difficult for the sake of Greece.

NEOPTOLEMUS

Ulysses! Why did you choose me? And what need had
you of me to do a deed my whole soul recoils from?

ULYSSES

Because it is a deed I personally cannot do. Philoctetes
knows me too well. If he sees me alone, he will suspect
some trick. Your innocence will be a protection. It is
you who must do this deed.

NEOPTOLEMUS

No, Ulysses. By Zeus, I will not do it.

ULYSSES

My boy, do not speak of Zeus. You have not understood me. Because I hide the aching of my heart, because
I consent to the deed, do you think I grieve for it less
than you? You do not know Philoctetes, and Philoctetes
is my friend. It is harder for me to betray him than for
you. The gods' commandments are cruel; they are gods.
If I did not speak to you in the boat, it was because in
the sadness of my heart I could not even think of words
. . . But you fly into a temper like your father, and you
are deaf to reason.

NEOPTOLEMUS

My father is dead, Ulysses; don't speak of him; he died for Greece. Ah! to struggle, to suffer, to die for her—ask what you will of me—but not to betray a friend of my father's!

ULYSSES

Listen, my child, and answer me: are you not the friend of all Greeks rather than the friend of only one; and again, is not the land of one's fathers more than a single man? and would you consent to save a single man, if in order to save him, you had to be the ruin of Greece?

NEOPTOLEMUS

Ulysses, you are right, I would not consent.

ULYSSES

And you agree that if friendship is a very precious thing, our country is more precious still? Tell me, Neoptolemus, what is virtue?

NEOPTOLEMUS

Teach me, sage son of Laertes.

ULYSSES

Calm your passion; put duty above all things.

NEOPTOLEMUS

What is duty, Ulysses?

ULYSSES

The voice of the gods, the order of the city, the sacrifice of ourselves to Greece; and as one sees a lover searching everywhere for the most precious flowers to offer as gifts to his mistress, wishing, indeed, to die for her, as if, poor wretch, he had no better gift than himself, and if it is true that your fatherland is dear to you, what could you find that would be too dear to give her; and did you not agree just now that it was only after her that friendship came. What was dearer to Agamemnon than his daughter, if it was not his country? Make your sacrifice as on an altar . . . but Philoctetes himself, in this island where he lives alone, what has he more precious than his bow to offer as a gift to his country?

NEOPTOLEMUS

Then, in that case, ask him, Ulysses.

ULYSSES

He might refuse. I don't know what his present temper may be, but I know that he was angry with the chiefs of our army because of his abandonment, and perhaps he himself angers the gods by his frame of mind and by having so vilely ceased to desire our victory. And perhaps the gods in their anger intend to chastise him still further through us. If he is forced into virtue by being obliged to give up his arms, the gods may treat him with less severity.

NEOPTOLEMUS

But, Ulysses, can the acts we do against our own will be meritorious?

ULYSSES

Do you not think, Neoptolemus, that the most important thing of all is that the gods' commands should be carried out, even though they may be carried out without the approval of every single individual?

NEOPTOLEMUS

I agreed with everything you said at first, but now I don't know what to say, and it even seems to me that . . .

ULYSSES

Hush! Listen! . . . Don't you hear anything?

NEOPTOLEMUS

Yes. The sea.

ULYSSES

No. It's Philoctetes! His frightful screams are beginning to reach us.

NEOPTOLEMUS

Frightful? I can hear nothing on the contrary but the most musical singing.

ULYSSES (*listening*)

It's true. He's singing. How kind of him! Now that he's alone, he sings! When he was with us, he screamed.

NEOPTOLEMUS

What is he singing?

ULYSSES

The words aren't distinguishable yet. Wait a moment.
He's coming nearer.

NEOPTOLEMUS

He has ceased singing. He has stopped. He has seen
our footsteps on the snow.

ULYSSES (*laughing*)

There! now he has begun to scream again. Ah!
Philoctetes!

NEOPTOLEMUS

Yes, you're right. His screams are horrible.

ULYSSES

Go and lay my sword on that rock, so that he may
recognise a Grecian weapon and know that the foot-
marks he has seen are those of one of his countrymen.
Make haste. Here he comes!—That's right.—Come now;
let's hide behind that mound of snow. We shall see him
without his being able to see us. What curses he will
utter! "Wretch!", he will say, "perish the Greeks who
abandoned me! Chiefs of the army! Thou, wily Ulysses!
You Agamemnon, Menelaus! May they in their turn be
stricken like me! O Death! Death! whom I call upon
every day, will you always be deaf to my lamentations?
Will you never come? O cavern, rocks, promontories,
dumb witnesses of my sufferings! will you never . . ."

(*Philoctetes enters; he sees the helmet and arms placed in the
middle of the stage. Philoctetes is silent.*)

ACT II

(Ulysses, Philoctetes, Neoptolemus. All seated)

PHILOCTETES

Truly, Ulysses, it is only since I have lived apart from others that I have come to understand what is called virtue. A man who lives with others is incapable, incapable, believe me, of a pure and really disinterested action. For instance, you . . . you have come here . . . what for?

ULYSSES

Why, to see you, dear Philoctetes.

PHILOCTETES

I don't believe a word of it and I care less. My pleasure at seeing you again is great and suffices me. I have lost the talent of searching for the motives of actions, ever since my own have no longer any secrets. In whose eyes should I want to appear what I am? My only care is to be. I have ceased to groan, knowing that here there is no ear to hear me; ceased to long, knowing that here nothing can be granted me.

ULYSSES

Why did you not cease to groan sooner, Philoctetes? We should have kept you with us.

PHILOCTETES

That could not be, Ulysses. When with other people, my silence would have been a falsehood.

ULYSSES

While here?

PHILOCTETES

My suffering has no need of words to be known, since I am alone to know it.

ULYSSES

Then, since we left you, you have been silent, Philoctetes?

PHILOCTETES

By no means. But since I no longer make use of my lamentations to express my suffering, they have become very beautiful; so much so that they are a consolation to me.

ULYSSES

So much the better, my poor Philoctetes.

PHILOCTETES

Oh, above all, don't pity me! I have ceased to long, I told you, because I knew there was nothing to be obtained. . . . Nothing to be obtained from the outside, it is true, but a great deal from myself; it is since then that I have begun to long for virtue; my soul is entirely taken up with it, and in spite of my pain, I am able to rest at peace; I was resting so, at any rate, when you arrived. . . . You are smiling?

ULYSSES

I see you were able to distract yourself.

PHILOCTETES

You listen without understanding me. Don't you admire virtue?

ULYSSES

Yes; my own.

PHILOCTETES

What kind is that?

ULYSSES

You would listen without understanding me. . . . We had better talk of the Greeks. Did your solitary virtue make you cease to remember them?

PHILOCTETES

Cease to feel angry with them, yes certainly.

ULYSSES

Listen, Neoptolemus! So that the success of the war for the sake of which . . .

PHILOCTETES

. . . you left me. . . . What do you want me to say, Ulysses? If you left me, it was to be victorious, wasn't it? So for your sake, I hope victory is yours. . . .

ULYSSES

And if otherwise?

84

PHILOCTETES

Otherwise we should have believed Greece to be greater than she was. I, in this island, you see, have made myself from day to day less of a Greek, from day to day, more of a man. . . . And yet when I set eyes on you, I feel . . . Is Achilles dead, Ulysses?

ULYSSES

Achilles is dead. My companion here is his son. What! Are you sobbing, Philoctetes? That peace you were so proud of . . .

PHILOCTETES

Achilles! . . . Oh, my child, let me stroke your lovely brow . . . It is a long, long time since my hand touched anything that was not cold. Even the bodies of the birds I kill, as they fall on the water or the snow, are as icy, when my hands approach them, as those upper regions of the air they fly through . . .

ULYSSES

For a person who is in pain you express yourself very well.

PHILOCTETES

Wherever I may go, I am still and always a son of Greece.

ULYSSES

But here you have no one to speak to.

PHILOCTETES

I have told you; didn't you understand? I express myself better now that I can no longer speak to men. My

only occupation between hunting and sleeping is thinking. My ideas which, in this solitude, are disturbed by
nothing, not even by pain, have taken so subtle a turn
that at times I find difficulty in following them. I have
learnt more secrets about life than ever my masters taught
me. I spent my time too in recounting my sufferings to
myself and, if my sentence was very beautiful, it was so
much of a consolation; sometimes even I forgot my sorrows in relating them. I understood that words were
more beautiful when they were no longer used for questions. As there was neither ear nor mouth beside me, it
was only the beauty of my words that I used; I cried
them aloud to the whole island, along all the beaches;
and the island, as it listened, to me seemed less solitary;
nature seemed to be like my sadness; it seemed to me
I was her voice and that the rocks in their dumbness
were awaiting it to tell their illnesses; for I understood
that everything about me is ill . . . and that this cold is
not normal, for I remember Greece . . . and I slowly
fell into the habit of crying aloud the desolation of all
things rather than my own; it seemed to me better, so to
speak, and besides that desolation was the same and I
was so far consoled. And then, it was in speaking of
the sea and its unending waves that I made my most
beautiful sentences. Shall I confess it, Ulysses?—Ulysses!
—some of them were so beautiful that I sobbed with
grief at the thought that no man could hear them. His
soul, I thought, would have been changed by them.
Listen, Ulysses, listen! No one has heard them yet.

ULYSSES

You have fallen into the habit too, I see, of talking
without any danger of being interrupted. Go on then,
recite!

PHILOCTETES (*declaiming*)

Innumerable smiles of the sea-waves . . .

ULYSSES (*laughing*)

But, Philoctetes, that's Aeschylus!

PHILOCTETES

Perhaps . . . Do you mind? (*Continuing*) Innumerable
sobs of the sea-waves. . . .

(*Silence*)

ULYSSES

And then . . . ?

PHILOCTETES

I don't know. . . . I am confused.

ULYSSES

Never mind! You'll go on with it another time.

NEOPTOLEMUS

Oh! do go on, Philoctetes!

ULYSSES

Dear me! The boy was listening!

PHILOCTETES
I can't speak now.

ULYSSES (*rising*)

I'll leave you to collect your thoughts. I'll be back
soon, Philoctetes. But tell me. Is there any captivity so

hard as to be without a moment's rest, a moment's forgetfulness, a moment's respite?

PHILOCTETES

You are right, Ulysses; one day I shot a bird and it fell; my arrow had only injured it and I tried to bring it back to life. But how hope to keep this aerial emotion which skims over the hardened earth where cold gives even the water, frozen as it is, the shape of my logic-fashioned thoughts! The bird died; in a few hours I saw it die; to keep it warm a little longer I smothered it with kisses and the warmth of my breath. It died of its longing for flight. . . .

It even seems to me, dear Ulysses, that the torrent of poetry as soon as it leaves my lips, becomes petrified and dies from not being able to procreate; and the inward flame that gave it life becomes fainter and fainter. Soon, though still alive, I shall become wholly abstract. The cold is overwhelming me, dear Ulysses, and now I am terrified, because I feel that in this cold, in its very rigour, there is beauty.

I walk with assurance on things and on fluids that have hardened. Without ever dreaming now, I think. I never taste now of hope, and am therefore never intoxicated. If, in this place, where everything has the hardness of stone, I set down—no matter what, be it only a single grain—I find it again, long after, exactly the same; it will never have germinated. Here, nothing becomes, Ulysses: everything is; everything remains. Here, at least, one can speculate! I kept the dead bird; here it is; the air is too cold for it ever to decay. And my acts, Ulysses, and my words, as if they too were frozen, are fixed in permanence, surrounded as with a

circle of established rocks. And as I still find them there,
day after day, all passion turns silent, I feel Truth becoming ever firmer—and I want my actions too to become
ever more and more solid, ever more and more beautiful; true, pure, crystalline, beautiful, beautiful, Ulysses,
like those bright and crystal icicles, in which, if the sun
were to appear, there would appear too in me the whole
sun, in all its entirety. Let me not stop a single one of
Zeus's rays, let every single one traverse me like a prism,
and may its refracted light make my actions adorable.
I want to attain to the greatest possible translucency, to
the suppression of my opacity, so that, beholding me
act, you yourself would feel the light . . .

ULYSSES (*going away*)

All right, Philoctetes, good-bye. (*Pointing to Neoptolemus*) You had better talk to him, as he seems to be
listening to you.

(*Exit*)

NEOPTOLEMUS

Philoctetes! Teach me virtue!

ACT III

SCENE I

(*Enter Philoctetes*)

PHILOCTETES (*in an agitated state of surprise and grief*)

Oh, Philoctetes, what blindness is yours! Acknowledge
your mistake, lament your folly! To think that the mere
fact of seeing Greeks again should have so enchanted
you . . . Did I hear rightly? Oh, yes! Ulysses was seated
and Neoptolemus was beside him; as they didn't know
I was near, they didn't even lower their voices. Ulysses
was instructing Neoptolemus, teaching him how to cheat
me; he said . . . Wretched Philoctetes! it's in order to
get hold of your bow that they have come all this way.
How much they must want it! Precious bow! Oh, the
only possession that is left me. And without it. . . . (*He
listens.*) Someone is coming! Defend yourself, Philoctetes!
Your bow is stout, your arm is strong, your aim is sure.
Virtue! Virtue! How much I loved you when I was alone!
In their absence, my silent heart had grown calm. Ah!
I understand now what that friendship of theirs was
worth! Is my country really Greece? Ulysses, I hate you!
And you, Neoptolemus . . . And yet, how he listened to
me! What sweetness! A child—as beautiful, ah! more
beautiful than ever your father was . . . How can so
pure a brow hide such thoughts? "Virtue", said he.
"Philoctetes, teach me virtue." What did I answer? I can
remember nothing now but him . . . And what does it

matter now how I answered him! (*He listens.*) Steps! . . .
Who is that? Ulysses! (*He seizes his bow.*) No—Neoptolemus.

(*Enter Neoptolemus*)

NEOPTOLEMUS (*calling*)

. . . Philoctetes! (*He draws near and as if on the point of fainting.*) Oh! I am ill! . . .

PHILOCTETES

Ill? . . .

NEOPTOLEMUS

It's you who have upset me. Give me back my calm, Philoctetes. Everything you said has taken root in my heart. While you were speaking, I didn't know what to answer. I could only listen. In all simplicity my heart opened to your words. And now that you have stopped speaking, I have not yet stopped listening. But now everything has become confused. I am waiting, in expectation. Speak! I have not heard enough . . . One must sacrifice oneself, you said?

PHILOCTETES (*unresponsive*)

Sacrifice oneself.

NEOPTOLEMUS

But Ulysses says that too. Sacrifice oneself to what, Philoctetes? He says to one's country. . . .

PHILOCTETES

To one's country.

NEOPTOLEMUS

Oh! Speak to me, Philoctetes; you must go on now.

PHILOCTETES (*evasively*)

Boy, do you know how to shoot with a bow?

NEOPTOLEMUS

Yes. Why?

PHILOCTETES

Could you string this one?

NEOPTOLEMUS (*disconcerted*)

You want . . . I don't know. (*He tries.*) Yes; perhaps.
—There!

PHILOCTETES (*aside*)

What ease! It's as though . . .

NEOPTOLEMUS (*hesitating*)

And now . . .

PHILOCTETES

I have seen what I wanted to see.

(*He takes the bow back*)

NEOPTOLEMUS

I don't understand you.

PHILOCTETES

No matter, alas! . . . (*Changing his mind.*) Listen, my
child. Don't you believe that the gods are above Greece,
and that the gods are more important than she is?

NEOPTOLEMUS

No, by Zeus, I don't believe that.

PHILOCTETES

But why not, Neoptolemus?

NEOPTOLEMUS

Because the gods I serve are only the servants of Greece.

PHILOCTETES

What! Are they in subjection?

NEOPTOLEMUS

Not in subjection. . . . I don't know how to say it. . . . But, look here! You see they aren't known outside Greece; Greece is their country as well as ours; when I serve her, I serve them; they are the same as my country.

PHILOCTETES

But *I* can talk about it—I who no longer belong to Greece—and . . . I serve them.

NEOPTOLEMUS

Do you think so? Oh, poor Philoctetes! One doesn't escape from Greece as easily as that . . . and even . . .

PHILOCTETES (*attentively*)

And even? . . .

NEOPTOLEMUS

Oh, if you only knew! Philoctetes . . .

PHILOCTETES

If I knew . . . what?

NEOPTOLEMUS (*thinking better of it*)

No, speak you! I have come to listen to you, and you keep asking questions. . . . And I quite realise that Ulysses' virtue and yours are not the same. . . . But when you ought to speak, you, who were so good at speaking just now, you hesitate. . . . Sacrifice oneself to what, Philoctetes?

PHILOCTETES

I was going to say "To the gods." . . . But it seems now that there's something above the gods, Neoptolemus.

NEOPTOLEMUS

Above the gods!

PHILOCTETES

Yes, since I do not act in the same way as Ulysses.

NEOPTOLEMUS

Sacrifice oneself to what, Philoctetes? What is there above the gods?

PHILOCTETES

There is . . . (*Taking his head in his hands, as though overcome.*) I don't know any more. I don't know. . . .

94

Oh! Oh! oneself! . . . I can't find word any more, Neoptolemus. . . .

NEOPTOLEMUS

Sacrifice oneself to what? Tell me, Philoctetes.

PHILOCTETES

Sacrifice oneself . . . sacrifice oneself . . .

NEOPTOLEMUS

You are crying!

PHILOCTETES

Oh, my boy! if only I could show you what virtue is . . . (*Standing up abruptly.*) I hear Ulysses coming! Good-bye . . . (*Going.*) Shall I see you again?

NEOPTOLEMUS

Good-bye.

(*Enter Ulysses*)

ULYSSES

Am I in time? Did you speak well, my pupil?

NEOPTOLEMUS

Thanks to you, better than he did. But what does it matter? Ulysses . . . he gave me his bow to string!

ULYSSES

His bow! Absurd! And why didn't you keep it, son of Achilles?

NEOPTOLEMUS

What is the use of a bow without arrows? Whilst I had the bow, he prudently kept back the arrows.

ULYSSES

Clever fellow! Do you think he suspects anything? What did he say?

NEOPTOLEMUS

Oh, nothing! Almost nothing.

ULYSSES

Did he go on declaiming about his virtue?

NEOPTOLEMUS

Though he had been so eloquent a little before, as soon as I began to question him he turned silent.

ULYSSES

There! You see!

NEOPTOLEMUS

And when I asked him what there is one can sacrifice oneself to if not to Greece alone, he said . . .

ULYSSES

What did he say?

NEOPTOLEMUS

That he didn't know. And when I said that even the gods (as you had taught me) were submissive, he answered, "Then there must be something above the gods, something . . ."

ULYSSES

What?

NEOPTOLEMUS

He said he didn't know.

ULYSSES

So! you see, Neoptolemus!

NEOPTOLEMUS

No, Ulysses, it seems to me I understand now.

ULYSSES

You understand what?

NEOPTOLEMUS

Something. For, after all, in this island which was so solitary when we weren't there, what was there for Philoctetes to sacrifice himself to?

ULYSSES

You said it yourself—nothing! What is the use of solitary virtue? In spite of all his beliefs, it is wasted without an object. Of what use are all his fine phrases, beautiful as he thinks them. Did they convince you? No, nor me either.

If he is living here alone in this island, it is, as I have shown you, to free the army from his groans and his stench; that was his first sacrifice; that is his virtue, whatever he may say. His second virtue will be, if he is as virtuous as all that, to console himself for the loss of his bow by thinking it is for the sake of Greece. What other self-sacrifice can one imagine if not for the sake of one's country? He was expecting us, you know, to come and offer it to him . . . But, as he might possibly refuse, we had better force his virtue, impose the sacrifice on him —in fact, I think the wisest plan is to send him to sleep. You see this little bottle . . .

NEOPTOLEMUS

Oh, don't talk so much, Ulysses. . . . Philoctetes just now was silent.

ULYSSES

Because he had nothing more to say.

NEOPTOLEMUS

And was that why he cried?

ULYSSES

He cried because he was mistaken.

NEOPTOLEMUS

No, it was because of me that he cried.

ULYSSES (*smiling*)

Because of you? . . . One begins doing a thing out of folly, and one goes on to call it virtue out of pride.

NEOPTOLEMUS (*bursting into tears*)

Ulysses! You don't understand Philoctetes . . .

98

ACT IV

(Philoctetes is seated, alone. He seems to be overcome with grief, or else to be meditating. Neoptolemus enters running)

NEOPTOLEMUS

If only I'm in time to find him! . . . Oh! there you are, Philoctetes. Quick! Listen. We came here to do something shameful; but be nobler than us! Forgive me. We came . . . oh! I blush to say it . . . to steal your bow, Philoctetes!

PHILOCTETES

I know you did.

NEOPTOLEMUS

You don't understand . . . to steal your bow, I tell you. Oh, defend yourself!

PHILOCTETES

Against whom? Against you, dear Neoptolemus?

NEOPTOLEMUS

No, of course not against me. I love you; I have come to warn you.

PHILOCTETES

And so you are betraying Ulysses. . . .

NEOPTOLEMUS

And I'm in despair. . . . It's to you I want to sacrifice myself. Do you love me? Answer me, Philoctetes. Is that virtue?

PHILOCTETES

Child!

NEOPTOLEMUS

Look what I've brought you. This bottle is intended to send you to sleep. But I'm going to give it to you. Here it is! Is that virtue? Speak to me.

PHILOCTETES

Child! the highest virtue can only be reached step by step. What you are doing now is nothing but a start.

NEOPTOLEMUS

Then teach me, Philoctetes.

PHILOCTETES

This draught was to send me to sleep, you say? (*Taking the bottle and looking at it.*) Tiny bottle! You, at any rate, will not fail in your object. Do you see what I am doing, Neoptolemus?

(*He drinks*)

NEOPTOLEMUS

Oh, wretched man! But it's . . .

PHILOCTETES

Go and tell Ulysses. Say . . . he can come now.

(*Neoptolemus, in consternation, rushes out, shouting as he goes*)

PHILOCTETES (*alone*)

You will admire me, Ulysses; I shall force you to admire me. My virtue overtops yours and you are lowered in your self-esteem. Virtue of Philoctetes, know yourself uplifted! Enjoy the satisfaction of your beauty! Neoptolemus, why didn't you take my bow at once? The more you loved me, the more difficult it was for you: your self-sacrifice has not been great enough. Take them . . . (*Looking round.*) He has gone . . .

That draught had a horrible taste. The mere thought of it makes my gorge rise; I wish I could go to sleep quicker. Of all self-sacrifices, the maddest is the sacrifice of oneself for others, for that makes one their superior. I am sacrificing myself, yes, but not for Greece . . . I regret only one thing and that is that my sacrifice will be of service to Greece . . . But no, I don't even regret that . . . But then don't thank me: it's for my own sake I am doing it, not for yours.—Ulysses, you will admire me, won't you? But will you admire me, Ulysses? Ulysses! Ulysses! But where are you? Understand me: I am sacrificing myself, but not for my country . . . for something else, I tell you; for . . . for . . . what? I don't know. Will you understand? Ulysses! Perhaps you'll think I am sacrificing myself for Greece! Oh, that bow, those arrows will be used in her service . . . Where can I throw them? The sea! (*He tries to run, but sinks down, overcome by the sleeping draught.*) I have no strength. Ah! my head is swimming. . . . He's coming. . . .

Virtue! Virtue! I try to find some exaltation in your bitter name; have I exhausted it already? The pride on which I leant is shaking, is giving way. My whole self is slipping from me.

"Nothing by starts. No leaps and bounds," I said to him. "No leaps and bounds!" To undertake what is beyond one's strength, Neoptolemus, that is what is called virtue. Virtue! . . . I no longer believe in it, Neoptolemus. But listen to me, Neoptolemus! Neoptolemus, there is no such thing as virtue. Neoptolemus! He can't hear me . . .

(He falls down overcome and goes to sleep. Ulysses enters with Neoptolemus and catches sight of Philoctetes)

ULYSSES

(To Neoptolemus)

And now, leave me alone with him.

(Neoptolemus, a prey to the most violent emotion, hesitates to leave)

Yes, yes! go away! No matter where! Go and get the boat ready, if you like.

(Neoptolemus goes)

ULYSSES

(He goes up to Philoctetes and bends over him)

Philoctetes! Can't you hear me, Philoctetes? Will you never hear me again? What am I to do? I wanted to tell you . . . that you have vanquished me, Philoctetes. And I can see virtue now; and I feel its beauty to be so great, that in your presence I no longer dare act. I feel my duty to be crueller than yours, because I feel it to be less august. Your bow—I cannot, I will not take it now: you have given it. Neoptolemus is a child: it is for him to obey. (*Neoptolemus re-enters.*) Ah! There he is! (*In a commanding voice.*) And now, Neoptolemus, take the bow and arrows and carry them to the boat.

(*Neoptolemus, in despair, bends over Philoctetes, then, falling on his knees, kisses him on the forehead*)

ULYSSES

I order you. Is it not enough to have betrayed me? Must you betray your country too? See how he has sacrificed himself to it.

(*Neoptolemus submissively takes up the bow and arrows and goes off*)

And now good-bye, relentless Philoctetes. Do you despise me very much? Ah! I wish I knew! . . . How I should like him to know that I think him admirable . . . and that . . . thanks to him, we shall be victorious.

NEOPTOLEMUS (*calling from a distance*)

Ulysses!

ULYSSES

Coming!

(*He goes out*)

ACT V

(*Philoctetes, alone, seated on a rock. The sun is rising in a perfectly pure sky. On the sea a boat is sailing away in the distance. Philoctetes gazes at it for a long time*)

PHILOCTETES (*very calm, murmurs*)

They will never come back; there's no bow for them to take now . . . I am happy.

(*His voice has become extraordinarily sweet and beautiful; flowers are springing up through the snow about him; birds fly down from heaven to feed him*)

BATHSHEBA

To Mme. Lucie Delarue-Mardrus

Bethsabé appeared in the Review *Vers et Prose* in the number dated December, 1908, to March, 1909. Its two first scenes had already come out in *l'Ermitage* in the January and February numbers of 1903.

DAVID, *King of Judah*

JOAB, *Chief of David's army*

(King David, dressed partly like a priest and partly like a warrior, is prostrate on the ground reciting a prayer which he has just finished composing)

DAVID

"Even the strong man faileth, the young man faltereth,
But he that putteth his trust in the Lord . . ."

(Enter Joab)

You are too early, Joab, I have not yet finished my prayer.
Do not speak. Where was I? . . . Ah!
                        "He will never stumble.
The Lord will lend strength to him that is weary;
His wings shall grow like an eagle's."
I had first written "their wings, like those of eagles, will
    grow . . ."
But "His wings shall grow like an eagle's" is better.
What do you want, Joab?

JOAB

The Hittite has come back.

DAVID

Who is this Hittite? From where has he come back?

JOAB

From the siege of Rabbah, and he has brought news of it.
For that matter he is nothing but an ordinary soldier
And the King . . .

DAVID

Pooh! Are you jealous of him, Joab?
Uriah the Hittite is the bravest of my soldiers.
I pretended not to know it; so as to hear you telling lies.
Shall I forget who triumphed over the Philistines at Gath?
Who defended the fields of Pas-Dammim against them?
Tell me. Who smote the two lions of Moab? He did.
And the four giants, Rapha's sons? It was he.

JOAB

Perhaps . . .

DAVID

And once more: At harvest time,
In the cave of Adullam, I sought in vain for something
cool.
The Philistines were encamped in the valley;
Bethlehem had been occupied by them for two days.
You know that at Bethlehem there is a well of fresh water;
I was athirst that day,
And longed for its water. . . .
Who was it crossed the enemies' camp?
Who risked his life to bring me a cupful?
Who was it? Answer me that.

It was Uriah the Hittite.
And it's in vain, Joab, that you pretend to have forgotten
  these things;
I should still remember them on the very edge of the
  tomb.
And I don't want it to be said that
The King can be served without recognition.
I intend that Uriah shall eat at my table;
All I possess is his.
I expect him in the palace. Let him know it.

(*Joab signs to a servant and passes him the King's order*)

He is Nathan's friend, is he not?

JOAB

The prophet Nathan's? Yes, Sire.

(*Joab makes as though to go out*)

DAVID

Don't go, Joab.

(*The King remains silent for a few moments*)

I'm afraid of the prophet Nathan. That makes you smile?
It's because you don't know his powers.
The people obey him;
I myself, in his presence, I am like a shy child;
When he says, "The Everlasting" it is as if one heard
  God Himself.
No doubt I have heard other prophets speaking;
They prophesy, and then they are silent;
This one's voice goes on.
I want to force him to be silent.
Dear Joab, I am afraid of Nathan.

There comes an hour of the day in which the strength
of kings weakens;
There comes a day in life when he who has been walking
feels weary.
I remember the virtues, the prayers of my youth;
It was I then who conversed with God.
I remember King Saul . . . I too, like him, I am beginning
to see the shadows darken before my feet.
It is no longer to me that the Everlasting listens;
He no longer speaks by my mouth,
It is no longer me whom He addresses.
But I cannot endure His silence further.
I want to force Him to speak.

Like a famished dog that gnaws a bone, bare of all its flesh,
Like a mother pressing to her breast her dead child,
All last night I pressed on my lips the name of my God:
Between my hands joined in prayer
I warmed what remained to me of faith in order to pray;
But lo! I heard above me what seemed the fluttering of
a wing . . .
It was the time when the lamp's flame wavers,
When the lamp's oil is giving out,
The time when the valiant man feels terror,
When the resolution of the virtuous weakens,
When kings and men are dizzied by the wine of sleep . . .
But my own soul had remained vigilant;
I had awaited God all night.
I heard above me what seemed like a breath,
The light spirit of God coming down towards me.
Spirit of God, what name shall I give you?
Joab, I have sometimes seen the dove fluttering about
its nest
Hesitating a moment: "Shall I settle?"

And still it hesitates.
Above my bed God's Spirit fluttered its wings,
It came down ever nearer.
Golden dove, soon perhaps my hand may catch you . . .
I stretched out my arm towards the bird;
Then I darted after it, pursuing it from room to room
As far as the stair that leads straight to the palace gardens.
The bird grew bigger and bigger; it shone like thunder,
From time to time it settled.
Then suddenly I felt my knees were without strength,
And just as I was about to seize it, my whole soul was
    overcome with terror.
It started off again; it bounded from step to step;
I wanted to seize it and durst not . . .
However high you mount, dove,
I will reach you there.

It was a little secret terrace
Which, I think, I had never seen before.
The bird of God had suddenly vanished
Into the open air.
It seemed suddenly to have carried away with it all my
    longing.
The moment was approaching when the sky awakens,
When the walls are colouring with blue;
The gardens at my feet were deep pools of shadow
Into which my clear-sighted eyes plunged through the
    mist.
To whom do these gardens belong, Joab? As for me I
    do not know;
But I know that that is where my palace comes to an end.
I bent forward, for I could not very well distinguish as yet
What the something white was that I saw moving at the
    bottom of the garden.

I guessed, because of the thicker mist, that a fountain
    was there;
Near the fountain a form was bending.
Was it a veiled woman? Was it
A white wing on the water side?
Yes, it was fluttering, it was quivering like a wing;
For a few minutes I thought I had found my bird again.
The sun which had risen forced me to close my eyelids;
When I opened them again I was dazzled by the light,
But there was nothing there but a woman.
She had stripped herself of her veils;
Her bare feet were in the water.
She had stepped in among the reeds
To the very heart of the fountain.
Into my own heart she had stepped further still.
As she remained bending down,
I could not see her face
And her hair was wrapping her shoulders with darkness;
But, through the reeds, I saw the quivering of her belly;
A flower seemed to bloom between her parted knees . . .
My heart rose in me up to my throat,
It was just going to burst out in a cry . . .

(*The servant who had been sent with the message to the Hittite
re-enters*)

SERVANT

Sir, Uriah bids me say to the King his master . . .

DAVID

Is he not coming?

SERVANT

He says: Am I the one to enter into the King's palace
And Rabbah is not yet taken . . .

DAVID

Very good. If he refuses to come I will go myself.
Take him this message, Joab. Tell him to prepare a very
  simple
Meal and to-night I will be his guest.

(*Exit Joab*)

SCENE II

(*David, Joab*)

(*David is seated, thoughtful and anxious; Joab stands, listening to him*)

DAVID

He has a little garden . . .
The table, on which the meal was awaiting me under
  the trellis, was white.
"Look," he said to me, "look at my vine and the shade
  it casts."
And indeed, the shade on the table was charming;
"The little wine I have comes from this vine;
Here is some of it, King David; a sweet wine, taste some."
And as his wife had come up,
(She is called Bathsheba.)
She leant over and filled my cup.
I hadn't recognised her.
And even, quite at first, I didn't recognise the garden.
She, dressed as she was, looked to me much more
  beautiful.
The dark flood of her hair
Seemed pulsing about her.

The face I did not know was smiling . . .
But the garden, Joab, what can I say of the garden?
It was no longer like the one I had seen in the morning,
Full of mists:
It was a secret place . . . I drank that cup of wine.
I have drunk many wines, Joab, but that particular wine
For a long time, I think, I had been thirsting for it;
It ran down into my depths like some profound happi-
ness;
It filled my heart like the granting of prayers.
I felt it give youth and strength to my loins.
Bathsheba smiled; the garden filled with light.
Everything shone with love and with Uriah's happiness.
"You see the whole of my happiness, King David," said
he; "it is a simple one.
It is all held in the hollow of a garden;
It is all held in the hollow of your palace walls.
Your palace protects me against cold, against winds,
Without even knowing it . . .
I, one of the least among your men,
Great King David, what am I in your presence?"

"Your strength is my protection against the Philistines,"
I said to him; "What am I in God's presence, O Hittite?
And yet I know you, you, one of the bravest of my men,
And from my palace roof I had noticed your garden;
It was pale and blue in the morning mists;
The sun was barely rising . . .
I had not been able to sleep that night,
And I had prayed so much that I was as though drunk;
As I went up the stairs, I stumbled at every step;
I was pursuing a dream, as if I were still asleep,
And dreaming of a marvellous bird, which flew
From room to room, and I grew tired with following it;

But, no doubt, by that bird God guided me
As far as that terrace,
Look! the one you can see over there.
I saw my bird again in your garden, Uriah,
As soon as the sun came through the mist;
Yes, the bird I was following . . . Are you smiling?
It was there—come, show me, near a spring;
It had pushed through the reeds,
And there, tranquil,
Sheltered, it thought, from prying eyes,
In the rippling water
It was bathing . . .
You, detained at the siege of Rabbah, you can't have
    seen it, dear Uriah,
But Bathsheba, perhaps——?"

And Bathsheba was silent, blushing.
And, leaning over the water, to hide her shame or her
    laughter,
She let all her hair come tumbling over her face.
Already daylight was sinking and the whole garden
    getting soaked in shadow . . .
"Uriah," I said, "why didn't you come to the palace?
Was it Nathan . . ." "I have not seen Nathan again, Sire;
Not since I came back from the siege of Rabbah.
King David, King David, proud Rabbah has not yet
    fallen!
And shall I rest in the King's palace
While your people are living in suspense?
No! As long as your warriors, O King,
Are languishing on the wrong side of the walls,
My place is in the camp beside them.
I am going back there this evening."
"Stay with us a little longer, Uriah;

How long will it take you to get to Rabbah? Only a
    few hours——"
The night was already closing in; we stayed then with-
    out speaking,
The sky was so pure that we could hear the spring
    murmuring,
And the darkness seemed, round Uriah, a quiet deepen-
    ing of his happiness . . .

But desire, Joab, desire enters the soul
Like a hungry stranger.

JOAB

But, King David, who prevents you?
Take this woman.

DAVID

Yes. That's what I did there and then, Joab.

He owns a little garden.
Smaller than the least of my terraces!
My hands are already so full of riches
And of happiness that they couldn't hold another grain,
But for the sake of that one little happiness of his
I would let drop all the others,
It is so small, that happiness!
It seemed I need only put out my hand,
Only want it in order to take it,
Only lay my hand gently on it
In order to have it . . .

JOAB

But Bathsheba, Sire?

DAVID

Yes, Bathsheba. Well, I had thought her more beautiful.
She was lovelier in her garden
When she was bathing naked in her spring.
Bathsheba! Bathsheba! Are you the woman? Are you the
    spring?
Vague object of my desire.
Joab, when at last I held her in my arms,
Will you believe it, I almost doubted whether it was she
    I desired,
Or whether it was not rather the garden . . .
And that wine! that wine I had drunk,
The wine of his little vine!
Did I drink all that he had? I am afraid so.
It was for that wine, I tell you, that I was thirsting;
I felt that it reached, that it moistened, drop by drop,
A parching corner of my heart.
You remember: that water of Bethlehem
That Uriah went to fetch for me one day that I was
    feverish;
That was the only water that could quench my thirst;
    that and no other:
It is for that happiness of Uriah's that I thirst
And that it should consist of so little . . .

Come, Joab! Enough. You see that it is impossible.
How could I not be the possessor of riches?
Take the woman back now
To the Hittite's little garden.
Everything would be all right if I desired nothing but her;
But . . . And besides I know he is coming back this
    evening.

So he will find all his quiet happiness
Just as he left it; at least so he will think;
For the trace of a ship on the waters,
Of a man on a woman's body, on a woman's depths,
Even God himself, Joab, cannot see that.
But yet, Joab, take care that the prophet Nathan does
    not come to know of it.

(*Exit Joab*)

SCENE III

(*The same room in the palace. King David is alone. Night*)

Is that you, Joab? . . . No. Nothing yet.
Am I to be left alone then till dawn?
And the night! Will to-night never come to an end?
I prayed to God; and I hoped I should fall asleep im-
    mediately after;
But will there be any sleep henceforth for David?
I wanted to pray to God and then I began to think . . .
The action that seems fair to the eyes of the flesh in
    broad daylight,
Woe betide him who sees it again with the eyes of the
    spirit at night!
Woe to him who cannot fall asleep at the height of his
    action as soon as it is committed!
Who recalls it again and again in the dark,
Just as a blind man caresses with his hands the face of
    a dead beloved in order to recognise it.
Shall I find rest nowhere? Joab! May God save us
From nights filled with neither sleep nor love.

Everything had been prepared to let me sleep; everything was silent
And everything was already asleep, in my heart, in the sky and on the earth,
And I myself was on the point of sleeping . . . Then the Hittite appeared.
He came out of the dark, suddenly; and I hardly recognised him.
He was only lighted by my bedside lamp.
How did he come in? The palace doors are shut.
He stood before me, without speaking and without taking off his cloak.
"Uriah," I said, "is that you? Answer me! Why have you come? What have you come for?
Have you taken Rabbah? No, I expect not.
I should know it already . . . Take off your cloak. I cannot see your eyes. Speak to me.
Speak, I say. Why do you stand motionless?
Who let you come? What do you want of me?
Your Bathsheba is expecting you. Your place is in her bed, beside her,
In your garden. Go away. Go back there. I want to sleep."

Why did he stop there without saying a word?
What did he want? Presents? He always refused them . . .
And he wouldn't even drink the cup of sweet wine which, seeing he wouldn't go, I offered him.
And his stay lasted and lasted throughout the night;
I thought at times that my bedside lamp was going out,
Or that the Hittite in the dark was disappearing . . .

Had he actually gone when the prophet Nathan came in?
Ah! I shall get no sleep to-night . . .
I told you so. I told you that Nathan was to be feared . . .

But, Joab, now it is God I am questioning: What will
    man do
If, behind each of his desires, God is lying in wait?

Then, as if he were tearing out of me myself each of
    his own words,
Nathan began to speak in the dark.
What did he say! I wish I could wipe out of my mind
    those words of his!
He spoke of a poor man who possessed nothing but one
    little ewe-lamb.
A ewe-lamb, I tell you, which he had bought and brought
    up;
Which he had watched growing, which lay in his bosom
    and which he loved.
"Enough, Nathan! I know; she is called Bathsheba.
Stop now." But he went on without listening to me.
"Near the poor man dwelt a man who was very rich,
Who had so many goods, so many flocks and herds that
    they could not be counted.
And there came a traveller to the rich man's house . . ."
"Enough, Nathan, enough! I recognise in him my own
    desire."
"He was hungry." "I did not know how to feed him."
"The rich man, then, who possessed so great a store of
    riches . . ."
"But nothing that I had then would satisfy my desire."
"Made as if his eyes were shut to his own riches.
It was towards the poor man's goods that he went."
    "Yes, that was what the wayfarer wanted;
Nothing else, I tell you, would have satisfied him."
In vain I tried to make him stop;
He went on talking as loud as if he were a king in the
    house.

"The little ewe-lamb which was the poor man's only
  possession, he took it. . . ."
"Stop, Nathan! Stop! Your rich man deserved the punish-
  ment of death!"
"The little ewe-lamb which was the poor man's only
  possession, he took it."
"And it was not even that that the traveller desired . . .
And you see! I have returned him his Bathsheba.
It was only with his garden's shade that I desired her.
It was Uriah's peace that I desired,
Amidst all those simple things which he left in order to
  serve me . . .
As for me, I am willing to repent, but what have I done?
At the time I desired her, Bathsheba bewildered me and
  I could see nothing but her.
But now . . ." Is that you, Joab?

*(Enter Joab, who stands without speaking in the dark beside
  the door)*

                              Yes, that's you.
At last! I was expecting you as anxiously as the dawn.
You have come from Rabbah? Has the Hittite come back
  with you too?
Is the town taken? No. Or you would have told me so
  already.
What did you do there? Did you carry out my orders
  punctually?
Didn't I tell you . . . Uriah was stationed among the
  bravest;
Brave among the bravest, he should have been in the
  front rank of all . . .
You don't answer . . . Did you place him very near the
  walls?

Too near? Then you all, all of you, fled, leaving him . . .
Hush, Joab! God himself must not hear that
And neither must I know it, lest I should never again be
    able to forget it.
No! no! Tell me he is asleep in his garden, beside his vine!

(*Dawn is just beginning to be visible in the palace. It casts a
    faint light upon Joab and shows behind him, just discernible,
    the figure of a veiled woman*)

What's that you're dragging after you, in the dark, and
    all in black?
                    Bathsheba! . . .
Go away! Take her away! I've told you I don't ever want
    to see her again . . .
                    I hate her!

THE RETURN OF THE PRODIGAL

To Arthur Fontaine

Le Retour de l'Enfant prodigue first appeared in the March–May number of *Vers et Prose*, 1907.

AS painters of old their triptychs, so I, for my own secret pleasure, have made this picture of the parable told us by our Lord Jesus Christ. Leaving indistinct and unravelled the twofold inspiration that moves me, I have not sought to prove either the victory of any God over myself or of myself over any God. And yet if the reader demand of me some expression of piety, he may perhaps not look for it in vain here, where, like a donor in the corner of the picture, I kneel, a pendant to the prodigal son, smiling like him, like him with a tear-stained face.

THE PRODIGAL SON

WHEN, after a long absence, weary of his way-ward fancies, and as it were, fallen out of love with himself, from the depths of that destitution he had himself chosen, the prodigal son thinks of his Father's face; of that not unspacious room where his mother bent over his bed; of that garden, refreshed with running waters, but shut in and walled, from which he had always longed to escape; of his thrifty elder brother, whom he had never loved, but who is still husbanding against his return that portion of his goods which, prodigal as he is, he has never been able to squander—he confesses to himself that he has not found happiness, no, nor even suc-ceeded in prolonging those wild delights he had pursued in default of happiness.

"Ah!" he thinks, "if my Father, who was angry with me at first, now believes me to be dead, perhaps, in spite of my sins, he will welcome me back; ah, if I arise and go to him very humbly, if I kneel before him in the dust, with ashes on my head, saying, "Father, I have sinned against Heaven and before thee", what shall I do, if raising me with his hand he say, "The house is open to thee, my son; enter in"? . . . And the prodigal, already piously intent, sets forth on his homeward journey.

When he reaches the shoulder of the hill and sees at last the smoking roofs of his home, it is evening; but he waits for the shades of night to throw a veil over his penury. He hears his Father's voice in the distance; his limbs falter, he drops to his knees and covers his face with his hands, for he is ashamed of his shame, though yet he knows he is the lawful son. He is perishing with hunger; in a fold of his tattered cloak he has but one handful left of those sweet husks on which he had used to feed, like the swine he had herded. He sees the house preparing for the evening meal. He can distinguish his Mother coming out on to the doorstep . . . he can resist no longer; he runs down the hill and makes his way into the courtyard, where his dog, not recognising him, begins to bark. He tries to speak to the servants, but they draw back suspiciously and go to warn their master. Look, here he comes! Doubtless he was expecting his prodigal son, for he straightway recognises him. His arms open; then the prodigal, kneeling down before him and hiding his face with one arm, lifts up his right hand for pardon and cries aloud:

"Father! Father! I have greatly sinned against Heaven and in Thy sight. I am no longer worthy to be called thy son; but at least, like one—the meanest—of thy servants, in some corner of thy house, let me live."

His father raises him and clasps him in his arms.

"Oh, my son, blessed be the day on which thou hast come back to me!" And the joy of his heart overflows in tears; he looks up from his son's head which he had been kissing and turns to the servants:

"Bring forth the best robe and put it on him, and put a ring on his hand and shoes on his feet. Bring hither from our stables the fatted calf and kill it; and let us eat and be merry for this my son was dead and is alive again; he was lost and is found."

And as the news spreads, he hastens; none but he must say, "Mother, the son we wept has returned to us."

The sound of joy, mounting up from the household like a song of praise, makes the elder son's brow grow troubled. And if he consents to take his seat at the common table, it is because his father invites and entreats and constrains him to. Alone, among all the guests, for the servants too, even the most menial, are invited, he shows an angry face.

"Why is more honour paid to the repentant sinner than to him—to him who has never transgressed?" He prizes order more than love. If he consents to be present at the feast, it is because he is willing so far to grant his brother credit as to lend him an evening's joy; because too his father and mother have promised to rebuke the prodigal to-morrow, and because he himself is making ready to admonish him severely.

The torches send their smoke up to heaven. The feast is over. The servants have cleared away. Now, in the night, where not a breath is stirring, the wearied household, soul after soul, go to their slumbers. But yet in the room next the prodigal's, I know a boy—his younger brother—who will spend the live-long night till break of day seeking sleep in vain.

THE FATHER'S REPRIMAND

MY God, like a child I kneel before Thee to-day
with a tear-stained face. If now I recall and tran-
scribe Thy compelling parable, it is because I know Thy
prodigal child; it is because in him I see myself; it is
because I hear and at times repeat in secret those words
that in the depth of his distress Thou hast placed on his
lips:

"How many hired servants of my father's have bread
enough and to spare; and I perish with hunger!"

I imagine the Father's embrace; my heart melts in the
warmth of that love. I can even imagine an earlier distress. Ah! what can I not imagine? My belief is this. I
am the very one whose heart beats when, on the shoulder of the hill, he sees the blue roofs of the house he
has left. Why then do I pause before running to my
home, before entering in?—I am expected. I can see the
fatted calf that is being got ready . . . Stop! Do not
spread the feast too quickly!—Prodigal son, I think of
you; first tell me what your Father said next morning
after the feast of welcome. Ah! though the elder brother
prompts Thee, Father, grant me sometimes to hear Thy
voice in his words!

"My son, why didst thou leave me?"

"Did I really leave Thee? Father, art Thou not everywhere? Never did I cease to love Thee."

"No quibbling! I had a house to keep thee in. It was
for thee that it was built. Generations of builders toiled
so that thy soul might find in it shelter and comfort and
occupation, a princely and worthy abode. Thou, the heir,

the son, why didst thou break away from the House?"

"Because the House shut me in. The House is not Thee, Father."

"It was I who built it—and for thee."

"Ah! it was my brother who said that, not Thou. Thou didst build the whole world and the House and all that is not the House. The House was built by others; in Thy name, I know, but by others."

"Man has need of a roof where to lay his head. Proud son! dost thou think to sleep in the open?"

"Is that so proud? Others poorer than I have done so."

"The poor—not thou. None can abdicate his riches. I had made thee rich above all men."

"Father, Thou knowest that when I left I took with me all the riches I could carry. What do I care for goods one cannot carry with one?"

"All that fortune thou didst take with thee, thou hast recklessly wasted."

"I changed all Thy gold into pleasures, Thy precepts into fantasy, my chastity into poetry, my austerity into desires."

"Was it for that thy thrifty parents took pains to instil into thee so many virtues?"

"So that I might burn perhaps with a brighter flame and be kindled to a newer fervour."

"Think of that pure flame Moses saw in the burning bush. It shone without consuming."

"I have known the love that consumes."

"The love I would teach thee refreshes. And after a little time what remained to thee, prodigal son?"

"The memory of those pleasures."

"And the indigence that succeeds them."

"In that indigence, Father, I felt I was near Thee."

"Did it need penury to drive thee back to me?"

"I cannot say. I cannot say. It was in the parching desert that I held my thirst most dear."

"Thy penury made thee better feel the price of riches."

"No, not that! Father, dost Thou not understand me? Love came to fill the place that was emptied of all else. At the cost of all my goods, it was fervour that I bought."

"Far from me then, wert thou happy?"

"I did not feel far from Thee."

"Then what made thee return? Say!"

"I cannot tell. Sloth, perhaps."

"Sloth, my son? What! Was it not love?"

"Father I have told Thee. I never loved Thee better than in the desert. But I was weary every morning of seeking the day's subsistence. At home, at least, there is food and plenty."

"Yes, there are servants who look to that. So what brought thee back was hunger."

"Cowardice too perhaps, and sickness. . . . In the end this hand to hand existence exhausted me; for I fed upon wild berries and locusts and honey. I grew less and less able to bear the discomfort which at first had quickened my fervour. At night, when I was cold, I thought that in my father's house I had lain warm and snug; when I was fasting, I thought that in my father's house the abundance of the fare had always been greater than my hunger. My strength failed me; I was no longer brave enough, vigorous enough to go on struggling, and yet . . ."

"Then yesterday's fatted calf seemed good to thee?"

The prodigal flings himself down sobbing, with his face on the ground.

"Father! Father! The wild taste of those sweet husks, in spite of all, is still on my lips. Nothing will ever make me forget their flavour."

"Poor child!" says his Father as he raises him. "Perhaps I have spoken to thee harshly. It was thy brother's wish. His word is law here. It is he who charged me to say to thee 'There is no salvation for thee save in the House.' But listen. It was I who made thee. I know what is in thee. I know what sent thee on thy wanderings. I was waiting for thee at the end. Hadst thou called me . . . I was there."

"Father! might I then have found Thee without returning?"

"If thy weakness was so great, thou didst well to return. Now go. Go back to the room I have made ready for thee. Enough for to-day; rest; to-morrow thou shalt speak with thy brother."

THE ELDER BROTHER'S REPROOF

THE prodigal son tries at first to carry it with a high hand.

"Big brother," he begins, "you and I are not like each other. Brother, we are very much unlike."

The elder brother then:

"The fault is yours."

"Why mine?"

"Because my life is the life of order; all that differs from it is the fruit or the seed of pride."

"And can I differ only by faults?"

"Call nothing quality that does not lead back to order, and subdue all the rest."

"I dread that mutilation. What you would suppress is also our Father's gift."

"Not suppress—subdue, I said."

"I understand. But so it was that I subdued my virtues."

"And that is why I can still see them in you. You must increase them. Understand me though. It is no diminution of yourself, but an exaltation rather that I propose; all the most diverse, the most unruly elements of the flesh and the spirit should join together as in a symphony, where what is worst in you must go to feed what is best, what is best must submit to . . ."

"It was exaltation too that I sought—that I found in the desert—and not very different, perhaps, from the one you propose."

"Say rather the one I would impose."

"Our Father did not speak so harshly."

"I know what the Father said. It was vague. He does not express himself as clearly as of old; so that He can be made to say what one pleases. But I know what he means. I alone am able to interpret him to his servants, and he who would understand the Father must listen to me."

"I understood him easily enough without you."

"So you thought, but you did not understand aright. There are not different ways of understanding the Father; there are not different ways of obeying him. There are not different ways of loving him; so that we may all be united in his love."

"In his House."

"Love of him brings us back to it. You see it is so, since you are back again. Tell me now what made you leave it?"

"I felt too strongly that the House is not the whole of the universe. I myself am not entirely in the being you would have liked me to be. I imagined—I could not help imagining other cultures, other countries, other roads to lead to them—roads as yet untraced; I imagined in myself the new creature who would long to speed down them. I ran away."

"Think what would have happened if, like you, I had forsaken our Father's House. Servants and robbers would have pillaged all our goods."

"What did I care then, since I had a vision of other goods . . ."

"Which your pride exaggerated. My brother, indiscipline is a thing of the past. From what a state of chaos man has emerged, you will learn if as yet you do not know it. But he has ill emerged; with all his native weight he drops back into it, as soon as the Spirit ceases to sustain him. Do not learn it to your cost: the well ordered elements that go to your composition await only the lightest acquiescence, the slightest weakening on your part to return again to anarchy . . . But what you will never know is the length of time it has taken for man to elaborate man. Now that we have the pattern, let us hold to it. 'Hold fast that which thou hast,' says the Spirit to the Angel of the Church, and adds 'that no man take thy crown.' Thy crown is 'that which thou hast'—that royalty over thyself and others. The usurper lies in wait for your crown; he is everywhere; he prowls about you, within you, to encompass you. Hold fast, brother! Hold fast."

"I let go my hold too long ago. I cannot close my hand now upon my goods."

"Yes, yes. I will help you. I have watched over those goods of yours during your absence."

"And then those words of the Spirit's, I know them too; you did not quote them all."

"It is true; it goes on: 'Him that overcometh will I make a pillar in the temple of my God, and he shall go out no more.' "

" 'He shall go out no more.' It is just that that frightened me."

"If it is for his happiness."

"Oh, I understand. But once I was in that temple . . ."

"You did not find yourself better off for going out, since you have chosen to return."

"I know; I know, I have returned. I admit it."

"What good can you look for elsewhere that you do not find here in abundance. Nay, more! Only here are your riches to be found."

"I know you have husbanded my riches."

"Those goods you could not squander—the portion that is common to us all—our real estate."

"Do I then no longer possess anything personally?"

"Yes, that special portion of gifts which our Father will still perhaps vouchsafe you."

"That is all I want. That is all I will consent to possess."

"Proud brother! You will not be consulted. But let me tell you privately that that portion depends upon chance. You had better give it up. It was that portion of personal gifts that brought about your ruin in the first place. It was those that you began by squandering."

"I could not take the others with me."

"So now you will find them intact. But enough for to-day. Take your rest now in the House."

"I will, for I am weary."

"Then blessed be your weariness! Now go and sleep. To-morrow your Mother will speak to you."

THE MOTHER

PRODIGAL son, whose mind still rebels against thy brother's words, let now thy heart speak.

How sweet it is to lie at thy mother's feet and hide thy head in her lap and feel her caressing hand bow thy stubborn neck.

"Why didst thou leave me for so long?"

And as thy only answer is tears:

"Why dost thou weep now, my son? Thou hast been given back to me. All my tears were shed while I was waiting for thee."

"Did you still go on waiting for me?"

"I never ceased to hope for thee. Every evening before I went to sleep, I thought, 'If he comes back to-night will he be able to unlatch the door?' And it was long before I slept. Every morning, before I was quite awake, I used to think, 'Is not this the very day he will come back?' And then I prayed. I prayed so much that it would not have been possible for thee not to return."

"Your prayers forced me to return."

"Do not smile at me, my child."

"O Mother, I have come back to you very humble. Look how I lay my head lower than your heart! Not one of my yesterday's thoughts but seems vain to me to-day. Here beside you I hardly understand what made me leave home."

"Thou wilt not leave it again?"

"I cannot ever leave it again."

"What was it in the world outside that attracted thee so?"

"I don't want to think of it any more. Nothing . . . Myself."

"Didst thou think then thou wouldst be happy away from us?"

"It was not happiness I was seeking."

"What then?"

"I was seeking . . . to find out who I was."

"Oh! thy parents' son and brother amongst brothers."

"I was not like my brothers. Let's not talk of it any more; I am back again."

"Yes; let's talk of it. Don't think thy brothers are so unlike thee."

"My only care henceforth is to be like you all."

"Thou sayest that as though with resignation."

"Nothing is more fatiguing than to realise one's difference. I am worn out by my travels."

"Yes, it is true. Thou hast aged."

"I have suffered."

"My poor child! No doubt thy bed was not made every day, nor the table laid for all thy meals."

"I ate what I could find and often I had only unripe or rotten fruit which had to serve as food for my hunger."

"Didst thou suffer only from hunger?"

"The noon day sun, the cold wind of midnight, the quaking sand of the desert, the thorns that tore my bleeding feet, nothing of all that could stop me, but—I have not told my brother—I had to become a servant . . ."

"Why didst thou hide it?"

". . . of bad masters, who maltreated my body, exasperated my pride and gave me barely enough to eat. It was then I thought, 'Ah! if serve I must!' . . . In my dreams I saw my home; I came back."

The prodigal bows his head once more and tenderly his mother caresses it.

"What art thou going to do now?"

"I have told you. Endeavour to resemble my big brother; look after our property; take a wife like him . . ."

"In saying that, thou hast no doubt someone in mind."

"Oh, so long as she is your choice, no matter who will be mine. Do for me as you did for my brother."

"I would have liked to choose her in accordance with thy own heart."

"What does it matter? My heart's choice had been made. I renounce the pride that took me away from you. Guide my choice. I submit, I tell you. I will teach my children to submit too; and so I shall think my venture less fruitless."

"Listen; there is even now a child who might already be thy concern."

"What do you mean? Of whom are you speaking?"

"Of thy younger brother who was not ten years old when thou left us; thou didst hardly recognise him, but yet . . ."

"Go on, Mother. What is your anxiety now?"

"And yet thou mightest have recognised thyself in him, for he is the living image of what thou wert when thou left us."

"The image of me?"

"Of what thou wert, I said, not yet, alas! of what thou hast become."

"What he will become."

"What he must be made to become without delay. Speak to him; he will listen to thee, I doubt not, to thee, the prodigal. Tell him what bitter disillusion awaited thee on thy way; spare him . . ."

"But why are you so alarmed about my brother? Perhaps a mere likeness of features . . ."

"No, no; the likeness between you is deeper than that.

I am anxious about him now for what did not at first make me anxious enough about thee. He reads too much and his preference does not always go to the best books."

"Is that all?"

"He often climbs to the highest spot in the garden, where, as thou knowest, the open country can be seen on the other side of the walls."

"I remember. Is that all?"

"He is much less often with us than down at the farm."

"Ah! What does he do there?"

"Nothing wrong. But it is not so much the farm people he frequents as rough fellows as unlike us as possible, and others who are not even our countrymen. There is one in particular who comes from a long way off and who tells him stories."

"Ah! the swineherd."

"Yes. Didst thou know him too? . . . Thy brother follows him to the pig-sties every evening to listen to his stories; he comes back only just in time for dinner, with no appetite and his clothes reeking of the farm. Remonstrances are of no avail; severity only makes him more impatient of control. Some mornings at daybreak, before any of us are up, he hurries off to meet the swineherd when he is on his way out to graze his herd, and goes with him as far as the gate."

"But he knows that *he* must not go out."

"Thou didst know it too! One day he will escape me, I feel sure. One day he will leave. . . ."

"No, I will speak to him, Mother. Do not be afraid."

"I know he will listen to much from thee. Didst thou see how he looked at thee that first evening? What glamour thy rags cast on thee! And then that purple robe thy Father put round thee. I feared that in his mind he confounded the one with the others and that it was

141

perhaps the rags he found the most alluring. But now I see it was folly to think so; for if thou, my child, hadst foreseen such wretchedness, thou wouldst surely not have left us?"

"I cannot think how I could ever have left *you*, my Mother."

"Well, tell him so."

"I will tell him so to-morrow evening. Now kiss me on the forehead as you used to when I was a little child and you watched me fall asleep. I am sleepy."

"To bed then and to sleep. I will go pray for you all."

DIALOGUE WITH THE YOUNGER BROTHER

THERE is, next door to the prodigal's, a not un-spacious room with bare walls. The prodigal, lamp in hand, goes up to the bed, where his younger brother is lying, his face turned to the wall. He begins in a low voice so as not to disturb him if the boy is asleep.

"I want to speak to you, brother."

"Well, what prevents you?"

"I thought perhaps you were asleep."

"There is no need to sleep in order to dream."

"You were dreaming? Of what?"

"What is that to you? If I do not understand my own dreams, it is not likely, I imagine, that you will."

"They are very subtle then? If you were to tell me them, I would try to."

"Do you choose your dreams? Mine come as they will and are freer than I . . . What have you come here for? Why do you disturb me in my sleep?"

"You are not asleep, and I have come to talk to you gently."

"What have you to say to me?"

"Nothing, if that is the tone you take."

"Then good-bye."

The prodigal goes towards the door, but puts the lamp down on the floor, so that the room is barely lighted; then he goes back and sitting down on the edge of the bed in the dark, strokes the boy's forehead long and fondly; but he still keeps it turned away.

"You answer me more unkindly than ever I did your brother. Yet I too rebelled against him."

The headstrong boy suddenly sits up.

"Oh! Is it my brother who has sent you?"

"No, my child. Not he but our Mother."

"Ah! You would not have come of your own accord."

"But yet I come as a friend."

Half sitting up in his bed, the boy looks long and fixedly at the prodigal.

"How can one of my people be a friend of mine?"

"You misjudge our brother."

"Don't speak of him! I hate him . . . My whole heart is impatient of him. It is because of him that I answered you unkindly."

"What do you mean by that?"

"You would not understand."

"Tell me all the same. . . ."

The Prodigal lulls his brother in his arms and soon the boy's resistance yields.

"The evening you came back I could not sleep. All night long I thought, I had another brother and I did not know it. . . . That was why my heart beat so when I saw you from the courtyard of the house advancing, clothed in all your glory."

"Alas! It was in rags that I was clothed."

"Yes, I saw you; but they were glorious rags. And I saw what our Father did; he put a ring on your finger— a ring finer than any our brother possesses. I would not question anyone about you; I only knew that you had come from a long way off, and your eyes at table . . ."

"Were you at the feast?"

"Oh! I know you did not see me; all through supper you looked into the distance with unseeing eyes. And, that you should have gone to speak to our Father on the second night was right enough, but on the third . . ."

"Go on."

"Ah! If it had only been a single loving word, you might at least have given me that!"

"Were you expecting me then?"

"Oh! so eagerly! Do you think I should hate our brother so much if you had not gone to talk to him that evening and for so long? What could you have said to each other? You must know that if you are like me, you can have nothing in common with him."

"I had behaved very wrongly towards him."

"Is it possible?"

"At any rate towards our Father and Mother. You know that I ran away from home."

"Yes, I know. It was a long time ago, wasn't it?"

"When I was about your age."

"Ah! And is that what you call behaving wrongly?"

"Yes. That was my wrong-doing, my sin."

"When you left, did you feel you were doing wrong?"

"No. I felt a kind of obligation to leave."

"What happened after that? To change what was right then into wrong now?"

"I suffered."

"And is that what makes you say 'I did wrong'?"

"No, not exactly. That is what made me reflect."

"Then before that you had not reflected?"

"Yes; but my feeble reason allowed itself to be overcome by my desires."

"As afterwards by your suffering. So that now you have come back . . . vanquished."

"No; not exactly—resigned."

"Well, at any rate, you have renounced being what you wished to be."

"What my pride had persuaded me I was."

The boy is silent for a moment, and then suddenly cries with a sob:

"Brother! I am the child you were when you started. Oh, tell me! Did you then find nothing on the way but disappointment? All that I divine in the outer world different from here, is it really then mere illusion? All the new things I feel in myself, are they nothing but folly? Tell me: what did you meet on the way that made you despair? Oh! what made you come back?"

"The freedom I was seeking I lost. I became a captive and was forced to serve."

"I am a captive here too."

"Yes, but to serve bad masters! Here, it is your parents you serve."

"Ah! If serve one must, may one not be free at least to choose one's slavery?"

"I had hoped so. As far as my feet could carry me, like Saul in search of his asses, I travelled in search of my desire; but where he found a kingdom awaiting him, I met with nothing but wretchedness. And yet . . ."

"Did you not mistake the road?"

"I walked straight on."

"Are you sure? And yet there are other kingdoms, other lands without a king still left to be discovered."

"Who told you so?"

"I know it. I feel it. I feel I am already lord of them."

"Proud boy!"

"Ah! Ah! That's a saying of our brother's. Why should you repeat it to me now? Why did you not keep your pride? You would not have come back."

"Then I might never have known you."

"Yes, yes! I should have joined you out there. You would have recognised me as your brother; and even I still feel that it is to find you that I am leaving."

"You are leaving?"

"Hadn't you guessed it? Don't you yourself encourage me to leave?"

"I wish I could spare your coming back—but that would be to spare your leaving."

"No, no; don't say that to me. That is not what you mean. You started out, did you not, as a conqueror?"

"And that is what made my slavery seem harder."

"Then why did you submit to it? Were you already so tired?"

"No, not then; but I lost confidence."

"What do you mean?"

"Lost confidence in everything, in myself; I wanted to stop, to settle somewhere; the comfort that master of mine offered me was a temptation . . . yes, I see it now all too well; I fell short."

The prodigal bows his head and hides his eyes with his hand.

"But to begin with?"

"I walked a long while through vast spaces of wild, unsubjugated country."

"The desert?"

"It wasn't always the desert."

"What were you looking for?"

"I don't know myself now."

"Get up from my bed. Look on the table beside it. There, near that torn book."

"I see a cleft pomegranate."

"The swineherd brought it me the other evening, when he hadn't been in for three days."

"Yes, it is a wild pomegranate."

"I know; it is almost unbearably sour; and yet I feel that if I were thirsty enough, I should set my teeth in it."

"Ah! then now I can tell you: it was that thirst I was seeking in the desert."

"A thirst which that sour fruit alone can quench. . . ."

"No; but a fruit that makes one love one's thirst."

"Do you know where it grows?"

"In a little forsaken orchard, which one comes to before nightfall. It has no wall left standing to keep it from the desert. A rivulet was flowing through it; some half-ripe fruit hung from the branches."

"What fruit?"

"The same that grows in our garden; but wild. It had been very hot all day."

"Listen; do you know why I was expecting you this evening? It is to-night I am starting, before the dawn. To-night; this very night, as soon as it begins to pale . . . I have girded my loins; I have kept my sandals on to-night."

"Oh! will you do what I could not?"

"You have opened the way for me, and the thought of you will be my support."

"No; it is my part to admire you. Yours must be to forget me. What are you taking with you?"

"You know that as the youngest son, I have no share in the inheritance. I am taking nothing."

"Better so."

"What are you looking at like that through the casement?"

"The garden where our dead forefathers lie sleeping."

"Brother . . ." (the boy has risen from his bed and winds his arm round the prodigal's neck—an arm grown soft and gentle as his voice)—"Come with me."

"Leave me! Leave me! I must stay to comfort our mother. Without me you will be all the braver. It is time now. The sky is growing pale. Make no noise as you go.

Come, kiss me, young brother; all my hopes go with you.
Be strong; forget us; forget me. May you never return.
. . . Go down quietly, quietly. I have the lamp. . . ."
    "Oh, give me your hand as far as the door."
    "Take care as you go down the steps."

SAUL

A Drama in Five Acts

To Ed. de Max

ACT I

SCENE I

(*The King's Palace*)

*A vast, rather bare hall; right, doors into the inner apart-
ments of the palace; left, recesses closed by drawn curtains;
centre back, a wide opening gives on to the outside terrace; right
and left of this, massive columns take the place of a wall; the
centre place between the columns is filled by an enormous throne.
Between the columns the view stretches beyond the terrace over
gardens, where the tree-tops are visible. It is night. At the
back of the terrace King Saul is on his knees, praying. Near
him Saki, the cup-bearer, is asleep.*

*(Demons enter left, pushing aside the curtains. Others come in
from other directions)*

DEMONS

The King's palace, please?

1ST DEMON

This is the King's palace.

DEMONS (*laughing*)

Ha! Ha! That's a good joke! We all came together and
now it's you who show us the way! How did you get in?

153

1ST DEMON

Sh! Sh! Don't speak so loud. The King's there. (*Pointing.*)

3RD DEMON

Where? Oh, I see. And who's that beside him?

1ST DEMON

The cup-bearer.

2ND DEMON

What's the King doing?

3RD DEMON

Is he asleep?

1ST DEMON

No. He's praying. Speak lower.

3RD DEMON

I'm speaking low enough. If I disturb him, it's because he's not praying loud enough.

4TH DEMON

He does what he can.

1ST DEMON

Where are the others?

2ND DEMON

Here they are!

1st Demon

Hi there! Come in! Come in! Are they all there?

(*More demons come in*)

2nd Demon

One never knows. Some are still dawdling in the desert.

1st Demon

Now then! Is it true that he's had all our masters killed?

Several Demons

Yes; all! All!

5th Demon

Not all. He's left the Witch of Endor.

2nd Demon

Oh! she hadn't got any real demons. Only little toadlings who can't speak.

1st Demon

But the soothsayers?

5th Demon

All killed—all!

1st Demon

Then so much the worse for him! Since it's King Saul who has evacuated us, we'll take up our domicile with him.

4TH DEMON

But why has he had the soothsayers killed?

2ND DEMON

Clever fellow! He'll be the only person left now to know the future.

4TH DEMON

The only one, you mean, to try and guess it.

3RD DEMON

One guesses it such a lot that in the end it comes true.

6TH DEMON

What future is the most unguessable?

5TH DEMON

The one that never comes true.

(*They all laugh*)

1ST DEMON

Pack of idiots! Try to be sensible! We must first see about where we're going to lodge. After that you can crack your jokes. Let's settle that the fairest way possible. According to what best suits each of us. Answer now in turn. And one at a time. (*They squirm.*) You over there! What do you choose? Now then!

6TH DEMON

His cup. My name is fury or madness. It's me he'll find when he's looking for drunkenness.

1ST DEMON

Very good. And you?

5TH DEMON

I? His bed. My name is lust. I shall be there when he's looking for sleep.

1ST DEMON

And you? What's your name?

4TH DEMON

Fear—and I shall sit on his throne and make his hopes tremble like the flame of a taper with my breath; my name is doubt too, when he thinks I am whispering him advice.

1ST DEMON

And you?

3RD DEMON

His sceptre for me. It will be heavy in his hands and heavy on the backs of others when he strikes them with it; but frail and wavering as a reed when he uses it to support his weakness. I am called power.

ANOTHER (*at a sign from the first*)

I will take his purple robe, and my name is vanity; for he will be naked under his purple robe; and when the wind blows, he will shiver under his purple robe; and when it is hot, I shall be called indecency.

1st Demon

As for me, I take his crown, and my name is legion. And now, my dear fellows, we can laugh. Come! Pass me my crown. Lift up my purple train; carry my javelin, bear this cup before me, and see how a King runs— a King in all his glory!

(*He dresses himself up in the garments the King has left on the throne; the others form up in a grotesque procession*)

Take care! The King is stirring. Beware! The day is breaking! Quick now! To our posts! Away!

(*They put the King's robes back on to the throne and disappear as if into the inside of the throne. Saul comes slowly forward*)

SCENE II

SAUL

All the same, I am King Saul—but there comes a point beyond which I cannot succeed in getting to know more. Once there was a time when God used to answer me. But it's true that then I questioned Him very little. Every morning the priest would tell me what I was to do. That was the whole future, and I knew what it was. The future was what I did. It was I who made the future. The Philistines came. I was disturbed. I wanted to put questions myself; and from that time forward, God was silent.

What did he want me to do? In order to act rightly one must know the future. I have begun to discover it in the stars. For the last twenty nights I have been studying them patiently. But there was nothing there about the Philistines. . . . No matter, I have discovered something which has turned my hair grey. Jonathan, my son Jonathan, will not succeed me on the throne; my race will end with me. But who it is who will succeed me— that is what I have failed to find out—and for the last twenty nights I have been questioning. And this very night I even tried praying again. Nights in summer are too short. The heat is so great that nothing round about me is able to sleep—no one but my cup-bearer, who was tired; but I need other people's sleep; I am constantly being disturbed. The slightest sound, the faintest perfume distract me. My senses are open to the outside world and nothing delightful can pass by without my being aware of it.

Last night, at my command, my servants went out to kill the sorcerers—ah! all the sorcerers of Israel. This is a secret no one but I must know. And when I am the only person to know the future, I think I shall be able to change it. They're dead by now. I know it. About midnight, I felt my secret, which no one knows now but I myself, I felt it suddenly swell within me—take up more room in my heart—become oppressive. It is my possession! Come! Here is the day! Let everything now in the palace awake! I shall go to sleep for a moment or two. Last night I composed a few songs which I shall give the High Priest for him to sing and to have sung throughout the kingdom. (*He wraps himself in the purple robe, puts the crown on his head, takes up the sceptre and goes out.*) Ha! ha! I am still Saul, and I have servants in great number.

SCENE III

(Two servants come in carrying brooms on their shoulders)

1ST SERVANT

Well! did you see him?

2ND SERVANT (JOHEL)

Who?

1ST SERVANT

The King.

JOHEL

The King?

1ST SERVANT

For the last three nights we've found him here. Then he goes off when we come on to the terrace.

I don't know what he can be doing there, but he's that thin, he's certainly not saying his prayers.

(They sweep the room and then pull up the great curtain left. The daylight pours in)

JOHEL *(catching sight of the sleeping cup-bearer)*

My word! It's Saki! Hullo! cup-bearer! That's not a place to go to sleep in. Come on! Up with you! What are you doing there, my boy?

SAKI *(waking up)*

The King . . .

1ST SERVANT *(pretending to sweep him away)*

The King! *I'm* the King—King of sweepers!

(Saki gets up)

Yes! Let's talk of the King. He makes a jolly night of it here on the terrace, doesn't he?

JOHEL

Shut up, you idiot! Tell me, my boy, did the King spend the night here?

SAKI

Yes.

JOHEL

The whole night?

SAKI

Yes.

JOHEL

The whole night—and every night?

SAKI

The last ten nights at least.

JOHEL

And you, what do you do?

SAKI

I pour out his drinks for him.

JOHEL

And he, what does he do?

SAKI

He drinks.

1st Servant

Disgusting, all the same, for a king to get drunk.

Saki

Saul doesn't get drunk.

1st Servant (*chuckling*)

You don't pour out enough.

Johel

Shut up, you idiot! Then tell us, my little fellow. What does the King do all night here?

Saki

He says he would like to get drunk, but he can't, and that the wine isn't strong enough; then he looks at the sky and talks as if he were alone.

Johel

What does he say?

Saki

I don't know. I can only see he's very much troubled. Sometimes he kneels down as if he were going to pray. But then he says nothing at all. Yesterday he asked me if I knew how to pray and I said "yes". Then he told me to pray for the prophets; I thought he was joking and I said it was the prophets' business to pray for us. And then he said one must pray before becoming a prophet, because afterwards one couldn't any more;— and then he said other things I didn't understand very well, but they made him laugh and cry too.

JOHEL

And after that?

SAKI

He told me I must be tired and I had better go to sleep.

JOHEL

And did you go to sleep?

SAKI

Yes, I did.

(*Pause*)

JOHEL

Are you fond of the King, my little lad?

SAKI

Yes, I am fond of him, very.

JOHEL

Tut, tut!

SAKI

Why "tut, tut!"?

JOHEL

Tut, tut!

SAKI

Yes, I'm fond of the King. He's very kind to me. He told me to drink a little out of his cup, and smiled very sweetly when I said it was too strong for me. He talked to me. He said he was only happy at night, but he said even at night his day-time worries tormented him. He said he was happy when he was young and that he hadn't always been a king.

1ST SERVANT

You don't say so!

SAKI

Is it true he hasn't always been king?

1ST SERVANT

He was a goatherd like us.

SAKI

Then it's true what he told me, that once he wandered for a long time in the desert, for twenty days and twenty nights, seeking some she-asses which had gone astray; I thought he was joking, for he said the happiest time of his life was when he was looking for his she-asses in the desert—but that he never found them. And he said too that when he was young he was very good-looking, he was the handsomest of all the children of Israel, he said. He's still very handsome, King Saul, isn't he?

1ST SERVANT

A bit worn, King Saul. If he goes on like that star-gazing every night . . .

JOHEL

Shut up, you idiot! Go to bed, my little lad. After nights like these, the mornings can be spent only in sleeping . . . (*Aside.*) Nothing to be got out of this boy.

(*Saki starts going out. The 1st Servant snatches the wine flagon out of his hand*)

164

1st Servant

Hullo! Don't take that away with you! You're not going to sleep with that flagon! (*Saki waits.*) Off with you now! Good-bye! Good-bye.

(*Exit Saki*)

1st Servant (*drinking*)

He's mad.

Johel

Who?

1st Servant

The King. He's mad! (*Drinking.*) He's mad! It's all very well to spend the whole night drinking wine like this, or else saying one's prayers, if one's got something on one's mind one wants to get rid of; or else studying the stars to see what the weather will be like to-morrow. But all that at once! (*Drinking.*) He's mad!

(*He drinks*)

Johel (*absent-mindedly*)

Shut up, you idiot! (*Aside.*) The boy's too young and simple. We shall never get anything out of him.

1st Servant

Hullo! Here's the High Priest! It's when the King goes to bed that he gets up.

(*Enter the High Priest*)

High Priest (*to the 1st Servant*)

Go and sweep further off.

(*Exit 1st Servant*)

Well, Johel, have you seen the king? Did he say anything about himself? What have you found out? What have you found out? Tell me. I have come at dawn, before he sees the messengers, because I must know what's up in order to face a new situation. The messengers are back already; their abominable job has been done; and the clamours of the people will have woken the King, if so be he was still asleep.

JOHEL

No. Not still, but already. Every night, for a long time past the King has been sitting up on the terrace.

HIGH PRIEST

Out of doors? Dear! Dear! Alone?

JOHEL

Yes . . . No; with the cup-bearer.

HIGH PRIEST

The boy? Does he say anything? Come on! Out with it! What do you know?

JOHEL

You ask too many questions. And besides, I don't know anything.

HIGH PRIEST

What does the boy say?

JOHEL

Nothing to speak of.

HIGH PRIEST

He's too young. Does the King get drunk?

JOHEL

He says he can't manage to get drunk.

HIGH PRIEST

So we must think of something else.

JOHEL

Here's the Queen.

(*Enter Queen*)

HIGH PRIEST (*going towards her*)

Nothing yet, Madam. Still nothing.

(*Silence*)

QUEEN (*to Johel*)

Does he speak to the cup-bearer?

JOHEL

No; to himself.

QUEEN

And . . . what does he say?

JOHEL

The boy isn't able to repeat anything.

HIGH PRIEST

As I feared, Madam, he's too young.

QUEEN

We must find someone else.

(*Johel makes as though to go out*)

HIGH PRIEST (*calling him back*)

Johel! One moment! What does Saki say of the King?

JOHEL

He says he's fond of him.

HIGH PRIEST (*turning to the Queen*)

There, you see; he's won him over.

(*Exit Johel*)

HIGH PRIEST

No further doubt, Madam: the King has a secret. He's trying to read the stars. And if he has had all the sorcerers killed, it's because he has read the stars and wishes to be alone to know what they say. The Queen is aware, no doubt, that Saul spends his nights now on the terrace?

QUEEN

Oh, Nabal! How should I be aware of it?

(*The High Priest smiles*)

Oh! it's such a long time ago since Saul withdrew from me. To-day, Nabal, my anxiety has become greater than ever and I will speak to you more openly. Nabal! Saul never loved me. After he married me he made pretence of turning some show of flame towards me; but it was a very short-lived pretence. You can't imagine, Nabal, the coldness of his embraces! As soon as I was with child, they ceased altogether. I was afraid for a moment of being jealous, but I was mistaken; there was no need to be jealous: it was nothing. I know, I know he took concubines; but now he has repudiated them all—and then, Nabal, I must tell you about Jonathan. Jonathan is the only one who is his son. He dropped from me before his time, like an unripe fruit which decays without ever ripening. I was very slow to get over the disgrace I felt at having such a feeble offspring. He was early weaned and then I gave him over to the charge of men only, thinking that if he lived solely with warriors, he would grow in courage. So he hardly knows me. I am the Queen, not his mother. He is afraid of me, he does not love me. It took me a long time, I confess, to stifle every yearning of my heart, before I was able to devote myself, wholly, as I do now, to the difficult business of governing the kingdom. Saul is perfectly content to be of no help to me at all; his negligence is inconceivable; and yet he is always preoccupied. Nabal! Nabal! How I suffered at first when I saw the anxiety of Saul's brow stamped on his weakly son's. I used to follow him sometimes as he wandered about the gardens, or down shadowy corridors of the palace; I never saw him smile. And my hatred was turned against Saul, because it was through me that he had created this miserable offspring in his own hideous likeness.

HIGH PRIEST

And yet Saul was very handsome.

QUEEN

And so is Jonathan—very comely, I know. I know. His weakness has a kind of grace; but I hate his weakness, Nabal; I hate him! I hate him! I hate him!

But do you suppose I have disturbed you at your

prayers in order to talk about him? Listen! It is not the King's restlessness that torments me. I am glad to know him occupied. The cares of love are harder to bear, more wearing than those of royalty. The latter deliver me from the former. I like to feel my power too; and, besides, the King never claimed anything. All was well: the God of greater Israel too prospered under my government. And now, Nabal!

High Priest

And now!

Queen

We had him so well under control, Nabal.

High Priest

Yes, but for the last month, he has completely escaped us.

Queen

I feel I can't do anything unless I know what he is thinking. The Philistines are there, waiting. Saul alone can give orders; but I was in command of his will. I could do everything through him. At any rate he listened to everything I said through your lips. But now, as you say, he has escaped us; and while the Philistines are at our gates, neither advancing nor retiring, and enjoying the inertia of our men, he watches them from the top of his terraces, and seems busy with other matters.

High Priest

Yes; the Philistines are enjoying themselves, it is true. And even, to mock us the more, they have invented something: it's a hideous fellow called Goliath, who is a head taller than the tallest of them. For the last four days there has been a blare of trumpets early in the morning; a small soldier precedes the tall one and they march along the ranks of our army. Goliath calls out a challenge to anyone who is willing to fight him, and proposes the battle should be decided by this single-handed trial. Our army looks at him, no one says a word or makes an offer, so that every morning the giant's insolence becomes greater, his challenge more scornful and his insults more outrageous. He will soon consider he has already won the victory—a victory without a fight —a victory by agreement! Even our own soldiers now don't take themselves seriously; this war is merely a game: just a joke; as soon as the morning challenge is over, they fall into intercourse with each other; they break the bounds of their camps; they meet and mingle; exchange tools, gods, loves, wares; Saul continues to be silent and stony Israel becomes gradually penetrable.

QUEEN

And this giant, you say is called?

HIGH PRIEST

Goliath.

QUEEN

And you know no one to set against him?

HIGH PRIEST

So far no one.

QUEEN

And to take the cup-bearer's place?

HIGH PRIEST

The Barber's seeing to that. But why put anyone in his place? The King would suspect something. He's fond of the boy. We must make another place: a singer, a harp-player, something or other.

QUEEN

But who will get him to agree? He mistrusts us and won't admit any stranger into his presence. Jonas the Barber must undertake it. He knows how to manage him; he gets the King to listen to him.

HIGH PRIEST

Will he be coming?

QUEEN

Yes, with Saul, presently.

HIGH PRIEST

Here they both are!

(*Enter Saul and the Barber*)

QUEEN (*politely hurrying towards him*)

My Lord Saul, how have you spent the night? You look very pale, as if the moon were still shining on your brow. Believe me, you are wrong to spend the night on the terrace.

(*Saul makes an impatient gesture*)

The full moon in summer is said to have a pernicious influence on our thoughts. Since you have taken to spending the nights in this way, your brow seems to have become the abode of care.

SAUL

Oh, Madam, let me alone! It is since care has made its abode on my brow that I have taken to spending my nights so.

(*Enter guards. To guards*)

Well? And the messengers?

1ST GUARD

They are waiting for the King to call them.

SAUL

Where are they?

1ST GUARD

In the courtyard.

SAUL

With the crowd! (*Aside.*) I should have done it secretly.

QUEEN (*coming up*)

My Lord Saul! Is it true what they are saying in the palace? You have had the prophets killed?

SAUL

Not the prophets, Madam; the sorcerers. You know very well that God cannot endure them.

QUEEN

Then who will tell us the future now?

SAUL (*shouting*)

The King. (*To the guard.*) Let them come in now!

(*The guard goes out left. Enter Jonathan right*)

SAUL (*catching sight of Jonathan*)

Oh! Prince Jonathan. Good day. I am glad to see you in our presence at this hour. You will see what it is to govern. It is time you learnt. Come here.

(*Jonathan takes his place on the left of the King; the Queen on the right*)

QUEEN (*leaning towards Saul*)

Three more white hairs, my Lord! Barber, you are not looking after the King properly. You must dress his hair again as soon as the sitting is over. His face shows signs of fatigue and his beard is badly trimmed.

(*So saying, she goes up to the Barber. The guard re-enters*)

GUARD

My Lord, the messengers are here.

SAUL

Let them come in.

(*As the messengers enter, the Queen whispers to the Barber*)

QUEEN

Well?

BARBER

Well, Madam, I have found out . . .

QUEEN

Make haste.

(*Their voices are drowned*)

SAUL

Eliphas! It was to you I gave the list.

ELIPHAS (*one of the messengers*)

Here it is.

(*He hands the list to the King*)

QUEEN (*to the Barber*)

David, did you say?

BARBER

David, Bethlehemite . . .

SAUL (*reading*)

Two at Ramah; at Keilah, the invoker; three on Mount
Bethel and four on Gilboa; at the well of Sechu an inter-
preter of dreams; at Michmash . . .

(*He goes on reading in a low voice. The Queen goes up to the
High Priest and her voice is heard above the King's*)

QUEEN (*to the High Priest as though continuing*)

David.

HIGH PRIEST

David?

QUEEN

Yes, the son of Jesse, the Bethlehemite. Go quickly and have him fetched out of the camp.

(*Exit High Priest*)

SAUL

Well then, it's true? You struck them from behind, or, if in front, it was because they were asleep? So they didn't see you? They said nothing?

(*Jonathan totters*)

Why, Jonathan, what's the matter? Are you giddy?

JONATHAN

No, Father. We are learning to govern.

SAUL

Come, come. Lean on me. You must have a stout heart. And they said nothing? I can't ask everyone. I'm too tired this morning. Oh! I told you to have everyone's tongue pulled out.

ELIPHAS

We have got them all.

SAUL (*turning to Jonathan*)

Some of them talk after they are dead.

(*Jonathan faints*)

SAUL

There now! He's fainting! Ah! (*With an angry gesture.*) Madam, take him away! Out upon it! It's like a woman!

And it's because of him that I didn't question them properly . . . So! it's an understood thing, isn't it? (I really am very tired.) They've all of them been . . . And no one said anything? If, by chance, any of you heard anything, let him take care! But, in truth, everyone of you, my faithful servants, shall have his reward.

(*As he is speaking, the King passes his hand over his forehead several times, and then takes off his crown. He gets up and goes towards the door. The servants and messengers go out, leaving the guard and the Barber alone together for a moment*)

GUARD

But what's the matter with the King? Is he ill?

BARBER

No, no. I will see to him.

GUARD

But . . .

(*Re-enter Saul. Seeing that the messengers have gone, he signs to the guard, and says mysteriously:*)

SAUL

You're to have those messengers killed.

(*Exit Guard*)

BARBER (*to the King, as he is moving away*)

Allow me, your Majesty. Just the smallest little friction. Oh, Oh! I noticed that wrinkle just now from a distance. Two touches of this ointment and it will vanish.

(*As he is speaking he takes various instruments out of his satchel and settles the King in a chair to the right*)

And here are the hairs the Queen pointed out a moment ago. Oh, it's true they are a beautiful white. But the others are a beautiful black; and your Majesty's not yet the age . . . Your Majesty has kept marvellously young! In spite of all the worries of royalty. (*Saul makes a gesture.*) Carefully now! (*The Barber puts kohl under his eyes.*) Carefully! We must keep our good looks. . . . Never mind! We've been a little over-tired lately.

SAUL

I haven't . . .

BARBER

No, no. Don't move your lips. I've made a little mistake in the beard. Ah! I meant to tell His Majesty . . . I've just invented a new kind of water-ice . . . flavoured with aniseed. Yes! aniseed! Particularly cooling and a trifle heady. Ah! When His Majesty's thirsty if he'll do me the favour of ordering . . . And I was forgetting! How absent minded!

(*The Queen comes in quietly from behind*)

The little singer I had told Your Majesty about . . .

SAUL

You told me nothing at all.

BARBER

Nothing at all! What can I have been thinking of? A wonderful singer, Sire, who accompanies himself on his harp as he sings.

178

SAUL

Well?

BARBER

Well! I've found him! (*Wheedling.*) He's here!

SAUL

But who asked you to?

BARBER

Your Majesty! Your Majesty! The other day as Your Majesty was coming out of his bath, he cried out: "Ah! if only I could have a little music!" But Your Majesty's too tired now; Your Majesty doesn't remember.

SAUL

Oh! let me alone with your harp-player! I don't want anybody near me. Do you understand? Nobody at all. Just bring me your ices. I'm thirsty.

QUEEN (*drawing near*)

Why not listen to him, dear husband? A charming little harp-player! Beloved husband! A harp-player to soothe your melancholy.

SAUL

Ha! My lady Queen! If she proposes anything, it must be something that will do me harm.

QUEEN

I have already noticed that music—and even the war-like flourishes of trumpets—has an excellent effect on your enfeebled faculties.

SAUL (*aside*)

The woman detests me.

QUEEN

It often happens that the mind is distracted from its anxieties by the playing of a harp and easily lapses into sleep . . .

SAUL (*aside*)

I hate her.

(*He gets up*)

QUEEN

. . . or delivers itself of its impurities and rids itself in a few wandering words of . . .

SAUL

Hold your tongue, madam. I have heard quite enough.

(*Exit Saul*)

QUEEN

Well, Barber?

BARBER

It's no good, madam. We must give it up.

QUEEN

What! Give up! Pooh! Let's try at any rate. The King never knows what he wants. Let's wait at any rate till he has seen him.

BARBER

Here he is!

(*David and the High Priest come in conversing*)

QUEEN

He's very beautiful.

HIGH PRIEST (*in the wings*)

Fight Goliath! What an absurdity!

(*They come in*)

Would you believe it, Madam? This youngster wants . . .

QUEEN

I know. But he's much too young.

BARBER

He's the one . . .

QUEEN

Be quiet!

(*Exit Barber*)

Are you David? David of Bethlehem? Daoud, some people say.

DAVID (*pointedly*)

David. Yes, madam.

QUEEN

I was looking for you, David.

DAVID

I was looking for *you*, madam.

QUEEN (*irritated*)

And why, David, were you looking for me?

DAVID

To ask you to allow me to fight.

QUEEN

The giant? Is it serious, then?

DAVID

Do you mean the giant's challenge, Madam?

QUEEN

Yours, David.

DAVID

Do you doubt it?

QUEEN (*giving him a long look*)

No. But you are a child, David. Really a child. How old?

DAVID

Seventeen.

QUEEN

Seventeen! And have you been trained in the calling of arms?

DAVID

No. So far I have lived in the mountains. I am a shepherd. But though I haven't fought with men, I have fought with bears when they attacked my flocks—bears and sometimes lions.

QUEEN (*to the High Priest*)

It's true he looks strong. But it was in the camp they found you, wasn't it? How did you leave Bethlehem?

DAVID

Oh! only a few days ago and only for a short time. I just went to see my brothers and to take them as a gift from my father some honey cakes that he had prepared for them. I am younger than they are. *They* are in your army; but in your army no one wants to fight. They're all frightened. And they all laughed at me when I spoke of going to fight against Goliath. They wouldn't let me . . . (*angrily*) and even my brothers insulted me. That's why I wanted to find you.

QUEEN

I don't laugh at you, my noble David.

DAVID

Then will you let me?

QUEEN

Wait a moment.

HIGH PRIEST

What, Madam? You'll allow him?

QUEEN

Let's try. I like him, Nabal. Have we a suit of armour?

HIGH PRIEST (*smiling*)

There's the King's madam. It's never used now.

QUEEN

Prince Jonathan can't wear it.

HIGH PRIEST

No; but David is bigger.

QUEEN

Send for it.

(*Looking after the servant as he goes out*)

Who is that who has just gone by on the terrace? Wasn't it Prince Jonathan? Call him.

(*Enter Jonathan*)

QUEEN (*to David*)

This is my son, Jonathan. You'll love him like a brother. Eh? Jonathan? Come, children. Kiss each other. (*To the High Priest.*) Look how charming they are! What,

Prince Jonathan, you are smiling? I have never seen you smile before.

JONATHAN

It's at David I'm smiling, madam.

QUEEN

Of course. He's going to fight.

JONATHAN

Goliath! Is it true, David?

(*The armour is brought in*)

QUEEN

And here's the King's armour.

(*David takes the helmet and puts it on his head for a moment. He tries the weight of the armour in his hand.*)

DAVID

No. I'll fight as I am.

QUEEN

But it's madness, David.

DAVID

Excuse me, madam. All this weight would be less a protection than a hindrance to my courage. I fear nothing, knowing that the God of Israel will protect me. I will go as I am; with my sling, which I can use skilfully enough.

(*The servant who had brought in the armour and has been waiting takes it away again. The Queen and the High Priest look at each other*)

HIGH PRIEST

Madam, let's allow him to have his way. He looks very valiant.

(*They go slowly towards the back exit, leaving David and Jonathan in front*)

JONATHAN

David, take my sling, will you?

(*David takes it, examines it and then gives it back to Jonathan*)

DAVID

I'm accustomed to my own. It's a better one.

JONATHAN

Then take these stones.

DAVID (*same as before*)

They're not sharp enough.

QUEEN (*from the back of the stage*)

Come, High Priest. Let them settle it for themselves. We'll leave them alone. They're children.

(*They go out*)

JONATHAN

David, what shall I give you then? All the same, I should like . . .

DAVID

Prince . . .

JONATHAN

Oh! Don't call me "Prince". Call me just Jonathan.
No one calls me that, but always "Prince Jonathan".
Even my father and mother. I'm sick of it.

DAVID

My father and mother at Bethlehem call me "Daoud",
and, on the contrary, they're the only ones who do.

JONATHAN

Then what am I to call you?

DAVID

Call me Daoud too, like them. Will you, Jonathan?

JONATHAN

Go and be victorious, Daoud! I will watch you from
the top of the terrace.

ACT II

The same scene as in Act I, but in broad daylight. All the curtains are pulled back. Men are walking about and forming animated groups. Johel enters right with the Barber.

SCENE I

(A group of men)

1ST MAN

I tell you it was to see his brothers.

2ND MAN

No; it was to fight the Philistines.

3RD MAN

Oh! come now! How could he have known about it at Bethlehem? It's the Queen who sent him to fight.

4TH MAN

Yes, when she had seen him. But that doesn't explain how he got into the palace.

2ND MAN

He got into the palace?

4TH MAN

Nor how he spoke to the Queen.

188

1ST MAN

He spoke to the Queen?

(*Another man comes up*)

5TH MAN

Nonsense! He wouldn't have seen the King, if the Queen hadn't been looking for a harp-player.

(*Another man comes up*)

6TH MAN

He wouldn't have seen the Queen, if the King hadn't had a secret.

2ND MAN

Ah! the King's secret! Do you want to know the King's secret?

(*He leans over to the 1st Man and whispers in his ear*)

1ST MAN (*shouting with laughter, whispers to the 3rd Man*)

Do you want to know the King's secret?

(*He whispers in the 3rd Man's ear*)

Who wants to know the King's secret?

3RD MAN (*shouting with laughter*)

Ten groats for the King's secret!

(*Another man comes up as the last words are spoken*)

7TH MAN

Well! *I* have a secret, like the King.

(*The others gather round him*)

It's this! Before he died the great Samuel went to Bethlehem. He sent for little David and then, in a small court-yard, where hardly anyone saw him, he took some oil and anointed him, just as he had Saul. . . . Thirty groats!

(*Johel and the Barber come up*)

JOHEL

A secret which might well be worth more than that, old tell-tale!

7TH MAN

How much?

JOHEL

Your head, old rascal! Take care that no one . . .

(*They scatter and gradually disappear*)

7TH MAN

Ah! A poor reward one gets for one's confidences!

JOHEL

Does the King know that?

BARBER

Certainly not. Does the Queen?

JOHEL (*threatening*)

Barber! Take care. . . .

190

BARBER (*same*)

Johel! Take care. . . .

JOHEL (*changing to a sudden affection*)

My dear Barber!

BARBER (*same*)

My excellent Johel!

(*They start going out arm in arm. Shouts outside*)

But what's all that shouting?

JOHEL

It's David's escort going by.

(*They are joined by others who rush along with them*)

BARBER

Let's hurry!

(*The shouts below the terrace grow louder. Enter Jonathan and Saki, who go towards the terrace. Saki and Jonathan alone*)

SAKI

No, Prince, this way. You'll see better.

JONATHAN

Oh, Saki! Tell me again. All alone! With nothing but his sling! You saw him too! How magnificent he looked! He's my friend, you know.

(*Saul appears*)

But come on! Here's my father . . .

(*Jonathan and Saki go out*)

(*The stage is empty when Saul enters*)

SAUL

True, I can get solitude! But it's because people flee from me! Come! This Conqueror! Let him be brought before me! I am angry with him. I am very angry with everyone! These shouting crowds annoy me. These acclamations—denied to me—for an accidental triumph! They were not for me, even after my hardest victories. . . . Ah! My lady Queen, you choose your attendants! A child, they tell me. . . . Why? To reassure me? Who gave him the right to be victorious? You, perhaps! Not I.

(*He walks up and down as he speaks, and during the next scene continues walking. Guards appear at the door left*)

SAUL

Come on. Bring him in. So! he's a shepherd, this conqueror! It's true he's quite young. Ah! But he's terribly good-looking.

(*These three sentences are said in a lower and lower voice. Saul, as he is striding backwards and forwards, has so far seen David only from behind. He draws near and speaks loudly and angrily*)

But his hands are all covered with blood!

(*He looks him all over*)

Why! he's all stained with it! But he ought to have cleansed himself. You, guards! Couldn't you have told him so? Nothing stained with blood should be allowed in here!

(*David makes as though to go out*)

No! Let him stop! Little giant-killer, I'm very angry with you.

(*He strides up and down. After a short silence*)

DAVID

Why are you angry with me, King Saul? I was victorious, it is true, but it wasn't against you.

SAUL

But who allowed you?

DAVID

The Queen said . . .

SAUL

The Queen, ah! Let me tell you there is no queen in Israel. There is only the King's wife.

DAVID (*after a silence*)

Why are you annoyed, Sire? It is to you I am devoted.

SAUL (*aside*)

His voice falls upon my anger like the rain from Heaven upon the dust beneath! (*Aloud*) I wish to be left alone . . . (*David makes a move to go out*) with him.

(*The guards go out*)

SAUL (*still pacing*)

I look very angry, don't I?

(*David keeps silent*)

Come! Answer! Your name? What are you called?

DAVID

David.

SAUL

David. . . . David. . . . The Moabites say Daoud.
You'll agree to my calling you Daoud?

DAVID

No.

SAUL

No? Why not? Let me call you Daoud. I want to call
you Daoud.

DAVID

Someone else calls me that. I have promised that
only he . . .

SAUL

Someone else? Who?

(*David does not answer*)

SAUL

Little shepherd, I wish to know. I am your King.

DAVID

Your right goes no further than your power.

SAUL

Than my power? What do you do when one of the goats in your flock won't obey you?

DAVID

I strike it.

SAUL

Do you still refuse?

DAVID

Strike me.

SAUL (*raising his javelin and then changing his mind*)

Do you love God?

DAVID

My love of God makes my strength.

SAUL

Are you so strong, David?

DAVID

He is very strong.

SAUL (*after a silence*)

And now, what are you going to do?

DAVID

I'm going back to Bethlehem, my country.

SAUL

No, David. Listen. I want you in my service. The Queen has spoken of a harp-player for me; I don't want hers, but . . .

DAVID

It was me she meant.

SAUL (*after a moment's reflection*)

Ah! Then you can play the harp? But here comes the Queen. Perhaps she's looking for you. I'll leave you. I dare say you will have things to say to each other.

(*He makes as though to go out, but hides behind a column. The Queen comes in right talking to the High Priest. She catches sight of David*)

QUEEN (*to the High Priest*)

Here he is. Leave us.

(*Exit High Priest*)

Ah! David, I've found you at last and, thanks to God, covered with glory. At first, though I already thought you lovely, I still looked on you only as a shepherd. But now, made more lovely still by your triumph, it's only the victor I see in you. What is your anxiety, David? For you look anxious. I know the King spoke harshly to you just now. Is that it?

DAVID

No, madam; the King little by little calmed the harshness of his first words, and soon spoke to me very gently.

QUEEN

And for a very long time too? You were alone together, were you not?

DAVID

Yes; for some time.

SAUL (*in hiding*)

They're too far off. I can't hear anything.

QUEEN

Really, you would be wrong, David, to be troubled about such things. The King's mood need not vex you. It's not of much consequence; sometimes disagreeable, and even hostile, without any reason; and very changeable.

DAVID

But I am not troubled, madam. The King was kind to me.

QUEEN

I'm glad to hear it, David. It's true that your beauty cannot fail to be attractive; but what you call the King's kindness will be a great help to us in our plans. For I take an interest in you, David. Your courage deserves a better reward than the ovations of a stupid excited population. I see you will know how to deal with the King, since his gloomy mood was changed by talking to you, and—— But first of all, David, tell me, you won't forget that it's to me you owe this honour!

DAVID

What honour, madam?

QUEEN

Being singer to the King.

DAVID

Pardon me, madam, if I had heard already . . .

QUEEN

Ah! the High Priest told you?

DAVID

No.

QUEEN

The Barber then?

DAVID

But the King himself asked me . . .

QUEEN

Ah!

DAVID

You seem vexed?

QUEEN

Why vexed? On the contrary, David, isn't it an excellent thing that our wishes should coincide in you? And you? What did you answer?

(*They draw near the King*)

DAVID

It was just then that you came in, and the King went away before I had time to answer him.

(Still nearer)

QUEEN

Then, answer now.

DAVID

But the King isn't here, madam.

SAUL *(in hiding)*

Well done, my brave David!

QUEEN

David, your youth needs instruction. King Saul has not the authority you suppose.

SAUL *(in hiding)*

Ha! Ha!

QUEEN

In former days, I know, he was a king full of wisdom and courage; but now his will-power has outstripped itself; it needs to be guided, and in most cases it is I myself who make his decisions. Thus the idea of having a singer to wait on him is mine; he agrees; and so much the better, since the singer will be you. But understand too, David, that the King, harassed as he is with evil thoughts, needs me to watch over him constantly.

SAUL *(in hiding)*

Beware, madam!

QUEEN

But he speaks to me very little; I am hardly ever with him. His least words, his slightest acts, every thing about him may cast a light on his mental sickness and help me to care for him more usefully. So everything must be reported to me.

DAVID

Madam!

QUEEN

David, you mustn't take my words amiss. Without my watchful care, what would your King be worth? You will help me. Both of us, together, we may sometimes be able to cheer his fits of melancholy. You will know of them sooner than I and you will tell me of them. Then you and I together . . . Answer me . . . Oh! For a conqueror, you are singularly bashful! And you lower your eyes, while I raise mine—to look at you, Daoud—lovelier than ever!

(*She touches his cheek with her hand*)

DAVID

Oh! Madam! The King . . .

(*Saul leaps from behind the column. David flees*)

SAUL

Daoud!!! Enough, madam, enough! Can't you see that this child . . . Don't run away, David! I'm not coming after you, David, and look, it's not you I'm striking!

(*He seizes the Queen by her clothes and hair and drags her down on the ground*)

QUEEN

Jealous, perhaps! *You!*

SAUL

Oh, don't mock, madam! I am jealous, terribly!

(*He strikes her several times with his javelin*)

QUEEN

Detestable Saul! I didn't hate you enough, imprudent that I was! May the whole weight of your crown fall now on you alone! Cover up your anxiety! Protect it! Dangerous King Saul! Be dangerous henceforth to yourself alone! I shall see now whether you can hide your secret from the dead. . . . I didn't think it was so terrible.

(*She dies*)

SAUL (*bending over the Queen's body*)

You are wrong, madam. The secret you are looking for is another . . .

SCENE II

Saul's room. Ill-lighted by a single smoky lamp. Empty of furniture. Right, a bed. Left, a window. More or less in the centre a kind of throne, continued right and left by benches or anything that will make it possible to sit very near the throne. King Saul is discovered alone, dressed as before in a purple mantle. He is wearing his crown.

SAUL (*going to the door and shutting it carefully*)

Ah! I was waiting for the night.

(*He draws a curtain over the door, turns round and
looks about him*)

And now that I'm alone . . .

(*He sits down. The chorus of Demons looms up and immediately sits in a circle on the ground in front of Saul.
Their voices mingle with his*)

DEMONS

Let's deliberate!

SAUL (*not yet seeing them*)

It's quieter here than on the terrace. And Saki asked
me for leave to spend the evening with Jonathan . . .

DEMONS

. . . And David.

SAUL

Yes. For that matter, I preferred being alone. . . . The
perfumes out there distracted me; and I have nothing
more to look at in the stars. I see nothing more in them.

1ST DEMON

If he begins talking to himself, you know, it won't
be very entertaining.

(*He yawns and the others stretch*)

SAUL (*continuing*)

The sorcerers . . .

2ND DEMON

He goes on just as if we were not there.

SAUL

Perhaps they saw something.

4TH DEMON

We really must take a hand soon.

SAUL

What did they know? I ought to have kept some of them.

4TH DEMON

He doesn't let us get a word in edgewise.

1ST DEMON

Patience!

SAUL (*looking fixedly at the demons without seeing them*)
And here my mind stops short and I don't know at what particular point.

5TH DEMON

One might try some suggestion or other.

SAUL

I seem to be thinking with the greatest attention, but I don't know of what.

6TH DEMON

Then it must be of David.

Saul

They want to find out my secret, but I don't know it myself. I have several.

1st Demon

You needn't put yourself out with us, you know.

Saul

I understand now why I cared so little for the Queen. I practised chastity too easily in my youth. I practised a great many virtues . . . Ah! I was wanting to congratulate myself on having got rid of the Queen, and reflect on the advantages. . . .

7th Demon

We might also . . .

Saul

That's what I was thinking. Get rid of the High Priest too . . . There are more questions in Israel than he knows the answers to. When I ask questions, it isn't of him. There are more answers in Heaven than questions on the lips of men.

7th Demon

But . . .

Saul

—there are answers one has to wait for.

3rd and 4th Demons (*together*)

Or which one can't hear.

4TH DEMON

One makes them up.

(The two Demons fling themselves on each other and fight, but only for a moment and everything goes on as before)

1ST DEMON

Oh! I say, King Saul! Talk to *us* now.

SAUL

He pretends he loves God and that is the source of his strength. I am quite willing to love God; I did love Him once; but He withdrew from me. Why?

1ST DEMON

To let us get near.

(They laugh)

SAUL

My eyes are dropping with fatigue and misery.

5TH DEMON

You need a drop or two.

SAUL

Do you think so? No—not yet—and Saki isn't here.

2ND DEMON

But we are here.

SAUL

Ah! my faithful friends!

2ND DEMON

Come now, old Saul! That's the least you can say.

3RD DEMON

King Saul! We're thirsty.

SAUL

Yes, of course! I'll fetch the cup.

5TH DEMON

No, no, old fellow! Wait till it's brought.

1ST DEMON

Oh! let him alone. It gives him something to do.

(*They fight with each other. Saul gets up and seems to be wavering in indecision. The actor must give the impression that he is going on with his monologue*)

SAUL (*as the noise of the shindy increases*)

Don't make such a row, little ones. I can't hear myself speak.

2ND DEMON

But you're not saying anything.

(*They all shake with laughter. Saul can't stop himself from joining in the laughter in spite of himself*)

SAUL (*seizing the cup and flagon of wine, takes a little sip*)

Oh! this crown is in my way. . . .

(*He flings it off on to his bed and goes to sit down again; his purple robe slips away from his shoulders. As he is sitting down, he takes another sip and becomes aware of the Demons)*

Hullo! my little friends, you must be very uncomfortable sitting there on the ground. Come and sit beside me.

(They all get up and go and sit close to Saul)

1ST DEMON

Oh, you know. It's for you, not for us.

(Saul smiles)

2ND DEMON *(taking the smile for an invitation)*

Closer?

SAUL *(rather breathless)*

You're stifling me a bit like that.

4TH DEMON

No, no! It's because you want a drink.

5TH DEMON

Shall I pour it out for you? Make haste! The night will soon be gone.

(Saul holds out his cup. The Demon fills it and Saul empties it)

5TH DEMON

More?

(Saul holds out his cup again and the Demon fills it. As Saul raises it to his lips)

SEVERAL DEMONS

Hullo! What about us?

(*Saul lowers the cup. The Demons scramble round him and try to get hold of it so that the wine spills*)

SAUL (*getting up abruptly, makes the Demons roll on to the ground, where they stay. He drops the cup, and in a very loud voice*)

Oh! My mantle is all stained.

(*He walks up and down and then stands motionless; the lamp goes down and the dawn begins to whiten the window on the left. But the stage still remains very dark. A long silence*)

2ND DEMON (*his tone of voice completely altered*)

Saul, Saul! This is the hour when the goatherds let their flocks out from their stables.

3RD DEMON

Now, Saul, is the moment to go up on to the tower and watch the coming of dawn.

4TH DEMON

Or, on the perfumed hillside, in the freshness of the morning air, sing—sing a song of joy and praise.

5TH DEMON

There are lawns bathed in dew . . .

6TH DEMON

There are baths ready in the palace.

1ST DEMON

As for me, after a sleepless night, what I should enjoy most is an aniseed sherbet with a liqueur.

7TH DEMON

For me, it would be to listen to David singing.

(*They all laugh*)

SAUL (*taking his head in his two hands*)

Oh! to be alone! To be alone!

(*He opens the window, through which comes a slight glimmer of dawn—and stretches out his hands towards the open air. The Demons have gradually disappeared without any theatrical effect*)

God of David! Help me!

ACT III

SCENE I

Same as in Act I, except that the curtains left, which separate the room from the terrace, are drawn. Johel enters left and is about to cross the room. The Barber, drawing aside the curtain, enters.

BARBER

Hist! Johel!

JOHEL

Ah! Is that you, Barber?

BARBER

Have you seen David?

JOHEL

That's for you to say. I don't know him.

BARBER (*excusing himself*)

I know him so little.

JOHEL

Never mind. It's your business. You must keep your eyes open, Barber; keep your eyes open.

BARBER

We'll keep our eyes open, Johel! We will.

(*Silence. The Barber begins to weep*)

The Queen kept her eyes open too!

JOHEL

Too open.

BARBER (*weeping*)

Poor lady! Everything was so easy with her.

(*Silence*)

JOHEL

Amazing, that little David! He had only to show himself . . .

BARBER

To make a clean sweep.

JOHEL

To get it made, you mean.

BARBER

I had rather help sweep than . . .

JOHEL

Yes. But take care! It's Saul who sweeps.

BARBER

Interests are so . . . confused. On whose side to be?
Great God? Whose? I only want to do my best! We
must keep our eyes open!

JOHEL

Yes, Barber. We must, we must! But how on earth
did you get the idea that the King was lacking in will-
power?

BARBER

No, no. I never said that. I said his will-power was
out of sorts. It works by fits and starts.

JOHEL

Take care it doesn't start on us. Eh! That's what makes
it more alarming than ever. His decisions seem to have
no motive. Keep your eyes on the King, Barber.

BARBER

If you think it's easy! The High Priest . . .

JOHEL

Well?

BARBER

Well! He chatters with fright now when he speaks to
the King.

JOHEL

What! He chatters with fright?

BARBER

I mean his teeth chatter with fright of the King.

(*Johel shrugs his shoulders*)

BARBER

And then Saul now keeps people at a distance. In fact everyone goes off when he makes his appearance. And he's the one who does the spying now. One doesn't hear him coming and then one catches him listening behind a curtain—or one is caught oneself. And everyone slips off noiselessly, from room to room, where the King himself is going round noiselessly . . .

JOHEL

The deuce!

(*While the Barber is speaking, Johel goes to the curtain on the left and suddenly raises it*)

BARBER (*starting at the sound of the curtain*)

Oh! How you frightened me! As for me, *I* haven't got a sword.

JOHEL

Never mind, Barber, you must speak to the King; and whatever you learn . . .

BARBER (*looking at Johel's sword*)

It's wonderful, Johel, how strong our friendship has become!

JOHEL

And everything helps to strengthen it . . .

(*He ends with a gesture of girding it tighter*)

BARBER (*continuing Johel's gesture*)

. . . and tighten it. Oh! Here comes David! Be off! Quick! Leave us alone.

(*David comes in from the terrace. Exit Johel*)

BARBER (*mysteriously*)

Prince David! . . . Prince David!

DAVID

What is it, Barber?

BARBER (*panting as if out of breath*)

I have been running after you for the last four days without being able to catch you alone for a single second, Prince David!

DAVID

I am not "Prince", Barber.

DAVID (*more and more severely*)

Nor lord, either.

BARBER

It's because I don't know what to call such a glorious victor who . . .

DAVID

I was only victorious through the help of God, Barber. I'm not even a captain in the army.

BARBER

But your courage . . .

DAVID

Is no greater than my faith.

BARBER

Exactly: faith . . . but your hope . . .

DAVID

My hope is that, after having summoned me to kill Goliath, the God of Israel will be satisfied and let me return to Bethlehem and stay with my father and look after the goats as I used to.

BARBER

Oh! goats! It's men Lord David should look after . . . and that's exactly what I wanted to say. Quick! for anyone might come in! The fact is that King Saul is out of sorts and Jonathan is as feeble as a little rare bird, and neither of them is at all in favour with the people, so that if the prince wished it I, I, the King's Barber and doctor, who am in touch with him every day, I might . . .

DAVID

Then, since you have told me your secret, Barber, listen now to mine. It is this: I love Saul as my King and Jonathan better than myself; and I fear God, Barber, and you had better take care lest your words may have in them what is offensive to His anointed. You called me

"Prince" just now, which means you are ready to obey my orders, Barber. Leave me! Go!

(Exit Barber)

Jonathan! Jonathan! May the Eternal make steady this tottering crown on your weakly brow!

(Enter Saul and Jonathan. Saul is simply dressed; Jonathan clothed in all the insignia of royalty. David withdraws into the left-hand corner; Saul and Jonathan advance towards the throne without seeing him. Saul notices that the curtain has been drawn aside and very deliberately pulls it back)

SAUL

That's how I like to see you, Jonathan. Come! You must take my place on the throne to-night; it's high time you had a little practice in reigning, even in an empty hall. The sense one has of one's royalty is greatly strengthened by the habit of wearing the insignia. You must learn to get accustomed to them. The other day, when the messengers came, in spite of the extra weight of the crown, I don't think you would have fainted on the royal throne, if you had been upheld by the sceptre and by the sensation of the purple robes you are wearing to-day.

JONATHAN

Oh, father, let me be! I am so tired! If you only knew how heavy the crown is!

SAUL

Really now! Do you think I don't know! . . . But that's why you should start getting into the way of it at once. I am old; and the less firmly it sits on my head, the more important it is it should be fixed solidly on yours.

JONATHAN

Father! Stop! My head's aching. . . . Take back your royalty.

SAUL

No, no. I shall leave it you till this evening . . . Of course I shall keep it to sleep with . . . But for the present, stay like that in your purple robes, and while there's no one there, imagine you are reigning over numbers.

(*David makes a movement*)

SAUL (*turning again to Jonathan*)

Ah! Yes! you are really royal now! (*To David.*) I wasn't expecting you till later, David. Never mind! Stay now. Yes, the young King is practising. I thought that this evening there would be no one for him to reign over. But here you are! So farewell! I leave you with his royalty.

(*He moves away right*)

SAUL (*aside, and hiding behind the curtain*)

I'm glad he has seen me without my crown; it made me look too unapproachable.

(*David and Jonathan remain motionless until Saul is out of sight*)

JONATHAN

Daoud!

DAVID

O my young king! Triumphant king! How beautiful you are in all your glory! Why are you not Saul—and why wasn't it for you that I was called to sing still lovelier hymns! Or to stay beside you gazing silently? Or to fall down—thus—at your feet?

(*He gets up, laughs, and rushing to Jonathan, embraces him*)

SAUL (*raising the curtain, left*)

Gently! Gently!

JONATHAN

What makes you laugh, David, when you can see how horribly pale I am, and that I'm going to cry? And that I'm so tired that it's *I* who am on the point of falling at your feet.

DAVID (*stepping back*)

Jonathan!

JONATHAN (*rising and coming forward*)

Feel this crown. What a weight! Eh?

SAUL (*in hiding*)

A good spy-hole! Oh!

JONATHAN (*passing the crown to David*)

It has bruised my forehead. David! I'm ill. . . . Isn't it heavy? Oh! put it on, do.

(*He puts it on David's head*)

SAUL

Oh! I shouldn't have seen that. . . .

JONATHAN

How well it suits you! But it *is* heavy, isn't it?

SAUL

Oh! David! What? You!—You!

DAVID

My poor Jonathan! I wish I could think it heavier! But how weak you must be!

JONATHAN

It's true. It doesn't look heavy on *your* head, Daoud.

SAUL

You, Jonathan! You!

(*He falls on his knees and sobs, half wrapped in the curtain*)

DAVID

But you're unwell, Jonathan. You're pale and in a sweat. . . .

JONATHAN

This purple is stifling me! This girdle! This sword is too heavy for me. I still feel the weight of the crown on my head. Ah, Daoud, I wish I could let all these shows of royalty drop to the ground! I wish I could lie down on the ground and sleep! Oh! if only I were a goatherd like you, naked under my sheepskin, in the open air! How beautiful you are, David! How I wish I could walk with you on the hills. You would clear every stone from my path; at noon we would bathe our weary feet in the cool waters. Then we would lie down among the vines. You would sing. In what lofty words I would tell you of my love!

SAUL (*listening to this as if he were saying it himself and nodding approval*)

Yes.

JONATHAN

Night would fall; you who are so strong—here, take my sword!—you would defend me from the wild beasts. I want to rest in your strength! Ah, I am stifling! Here, take the purple. Undo this mantle.

(*He helps David to take it off*)

SAUL

Ah! I shouldn't be seeing this!

JONATHAN

Your shoulder looks whiter now! And my girdle . . .

SAUL

Oh, tortures! Mortification of the flesh!

JONATHAN

I don't know whether it's from joy, or from cold, or from the pains of fever or of love, that now I am shivering with only this linen tunic on me.

SAUL

How beautiful he is in the purple robe! Daoud!

DAVID (*as it were, calling him in a whisper*)

Jonathan! You are more lovely now in your white tunic than in all your regal finery. I hadn't realised your elegance nor the grace that weakness has bestowed on your limbs.

SAUL

Ah!

DAVID

Jonathan, it was for your sake that I came down from the mountains. Your flower of fragility would have faded there in the scorching heat of the sun. What! You are weeping! Shall I weep too out of tenderness? You are trembling? You are swaying? Comfort your weakness here, in my arms.

SAUL

Oh! Not that! Oh! Not that!

JONATHAN (*on the point of fainting*)

Daoud!

SAUL (*rushing out like a madman and shouting*)

And Saul, then? And Saul?

JONATHAN (*terrified*)

Fly, David, fly!

(*David, at sight of Saul, reluctantly leaves Jonathan and goes, not over quickly, throwing his regal attire behind him with horror. Jonathan falls, swooning*)

DAVID

Unhappy! Unhappy! Unhappy!

SAUL

And Saul?

(*He watches David's flight with stupefaction, and without saying a word; then goes up to Jonathan, kneels down beside him and lifts one of his arms*)

He's too thin! Come, Jonathan! Speak to me. Come now! It's your father! I frightened you, I know, but I don't detest you . . . (*Flinging down in disgust the arm he was holding.*) Ah! He's weaker than a woman! (*Bending over him.*) Is it love of David makes you so pale?

(*He runs right and calls*)

David! He is still running away. As if it was for him to be frightened!

(*He hurries to the curtain left, raises it and calls*)

Hullo there! Hullo! Someone! Someone! Come quick!

SCENE II

Saul's room. Saul enters conversing with the High Priest.

SAUL

So, not a single one? Not the smallest soothsayer left?

HIGH PRIEST

His Majesty knows that they were all cut off by his Majesty's orders.

SAUL

That's not the question. I'm asking you whether one small one wasn't perhaps overlooked.

HIGH PRIEST

Not a single one.

SAUL

It's not that I want to punish anyone, please understand. On the contrary, I should like one to have been overlooked. I want one . . . myself.

(*The High Priest is silent*)

SAUL

Oh! Well! Be off with you!

(*Exit High Priest*)

What am I to do? Nothing! Nothing! The smallest sorcerer would know more.

(*Suddenly running to the door*)

High Priest! High Priest!

(*The High Priest reappears*)

And your God? Is He always silent?

HIGH PRIEST

Always.

SAUL

All the same, it's rather hard lines! What have I done to Him? Come now, Priest, *you* answer at any rate. Why is He silent now? There must be some explanation in the end . . . Ah! I want to justify myself before Him. I am the accused; you, my judge. Question me.

HIGH PRIEST (*completely bewildered with fright*)

What?

SAUL

(How stupid he is!) How do I know? Ask me if I have frequented foreign women.

HIGH PRIEST

Yes.

SAUL

Why "yes"? I'm telling you to ask me whether I have ever lived with foreign women? Ask me, you fool! Or I'll . . . (*Brandishing his javelin.*)

HIGH PRIEST (*trembling*)

I ask you if you have lived with foreign women?

SAUL (*furious*)

No! I have not lived with foreign women. Do you hear? You know perfectly well I have not lived with

foreign women. (*Suddenly calm.*) Come on, now! Quick,
Ask another.

HIGH PRIEST

Another what?

SAUL

Ask me—— Really, you ought to know! There must
be some commandments or other.

HIGH PRIEST

There are the Ten Commandments.

SAUL

Well, then, say your Commandments. What are you
waiting for? Go on!

HIGH PRIEST (*reciting*)

I am the Lord thy God, who brought thee out of the
land of Egypt, out of the house of bondage.

SAUL

Oh! Make haste! I'm expecting the Barber.

HIGH PRIEST

Thou shalt have none other gods but me.

SAUL

No, not like that. Put them as a question.

High Priest

Hast thou made to thyself any graven image, or the likeness of anything that is in Heaven above, or in the earth beneath, or in the water under the earth?

(Saul shrugs his shoulders impatiently)

Hast thou bowed down to them or worshipped them? For I the Lord thy God am a jealous God . . .

(Saul yawns)

and visit the sins of the fathers upon their children unto the third and fourth generation of them that hate me, and . . .

Saul *(relieved)*

Ah! There's the Barber! You can go on with that another time.

(The High Priest goes out. Enter the Barber)

Ah! there you are, beloved Barber! Light the torches. It's getting dark.

(The Barber lights the torches and gets his apparatus ready)

Saul *(aside)*

I so much want to know that it's not David I need fear! I can't . . . I can't detest him! I want him to like me.

(The Barber signs that he is ready)

I sent for you because I want you to shave off my beard.

Barber *(stupefied)*

Shave your beard!

SAUL

Yes. My beard. It certainly ages me. It's time now for me to look a little younger. It'll make me look younger, won't it?

BARBER

Without the shadow of a doubt! But you'll look less respectable.

SAUL

I don't particularly want to look too respectable. Come now! Are you ready? I'm waiting.

BARBER

No! But really? Is the King speaking seriously?

SAUL

Really now, Barber. Do I look as if I were joking? (*He laughs.*) Yes, but you'll see how much better I shall joke without my beard. Seriously now, cut it off.

BARBER (*beginning to shave*)

Such a fine beard too! It's a pity.

SAUL

Pooh! I was hidden by it. One must make one's decisions without hesitation. How do I look, Barber?

BARBER

Tired.

SAUL

Ah!

BARBER

Yes. One can see His Majesty works hard.

SAUL

Yes. I had to work all last night again.

BARBER

Yes. Now the Queen isn't there any more, His Majesty has to busy himself much more with the important affairs of the state.

SAUL

There are affairs more important still than those of the state—and they concern me alone.

BARBER

Oh, yes!

SAUL

What?

BARBER

I said, "Oh, yes!" I mean, "Oh, yes!" . . . Of course, they only concern the King, and that's the very reason he's so tired, being obliged to take everything upon himself: perhaps too His Majesty is sorely troubled about certain things. It's true that if the Philistines . . .

SAUL (*enquiring*)

The Philistines?

BARBER (*finishing his sentence*)

. . . come back.

SAUL

Ah!—come back!

BARBER

The King must know that people say they are coming back.

SAUL

He knows, he knows; but . . .

BARBER

But—if I dare speak—the King is looking for a sooth-sayer?

SAUL

Ah! You know that.

BARBER

Ye—es.

SAUL

How?

BARBER

Does it matter?

SAUL

Do you know . . .

BARBER

Sh—sh—Oh! my scissors!
Hush! One moment! There!

(*He drops them*)

Unrecognisable! I have taken ten years off the King's age!

SAUL (*anxiously*)

Out with it! Do you know?

BARBER

Ye—es.

SAUL

A wizard?

BARBER

No; a witch.

SAUL

Where?

BARBER

At Endor.

SAUL

Ah! The Pythoness! How could I have forgotten her?

BARBER

What! Did you know her too?

SAUL

The one who talks with the dead? Yes, I saw her in times past; I had forgotten her, strangely forgotten . . . But she knows me. But you say I am unrecognisable?

BARBER

Let the King take a mirror; I have done.

SAUL

Yes, I don't look so bad! But oh! that wrinkle!

BARBER

Your beard hid it a little. Shall I try . . . ?

SAUL

No. Leave it alone. You may go.

(*Exit Barber*)

This time my passion serves my interest. I will go.

(*He goes to the window and opens it*)

The sky is lowering. There is going to be a frightful storm. All the sands of the desert have been stirred. No matter!

(*He leaves the window, casts off his purple mantle and wraps himself in an old cloak*)

Really unrecognisable! (*As if repeating a lesson.*) There is someone I must beware of.

(*He kneels*)

My God, grant that it may not be of David! I can't . . . I can't . . .

(*He gets up*)

Ugh! It's too long since I last prayed. And then when I prayed it was the same thing. We'll struggle. And it's not for me to take the first step. It was he who started by withdrawing himself. I want so much to know that . . . that it's not he.

(*The wind from the window blows out the torches*)

Ah! the wind! Let's go! Let's go!

SCENE III

The inside of a not very large cave. The entrance left back; on the right a hearth, the fire of which faintly lights the cave.

THE WITCH OF ENDOR

These four morsels of bread, these roots, and then, Witch of Endor, last of the prophets in Israel, die out, like a faint flickering flame. Those from whom I beg alms think themselves kind because they do not betray me to the King; they keep silent, but they give me no more food. King Saul, why did you cut us all off? But one day, do you remember, son of Kish, with no crown on your head, your father's goatherd, you came to me.

You were looking in vain in the desert for your lost she-asses; it was on that day that I, the first of all, foretold your royalty. And since then, they say it is you who have become a prophet. What do you prophesy? Do your lips too tremble, unable to keep shut beneath the horrible pressure of the future? What future is it that transpires through you and which you wish to be alone of all men to know, since you destroy the soothsayers? So be it! Let them keep silent in the tomb. But you, King Saul, do you keep silent? As for me, wasted away, I am departing. As over the margin of a well, thirsting for the unknown, men would hang upon my lips, whence prophecy came gushing forth. And men loved me not, for they would have made me foretell happy things and I foretold things that were beyond happiness. And now I think it is not good for man to know the future, for no mortal joy can last longer than the time it takes to say, "I am happy"; and we must make haste to say it, for all the rest of time is left in which to say "I was once happy"; and man's happiness is blind.

How cold I am! What frightful weather! All the toads of the neighbourhood have come to take refuge in my cave; such floods of rain, such an icy wind, that outside I thought I should expire even before dying of hunger. Never before have I felt so enfeebled. Who is it then who could have been so tormented by a longing for the future as to take to the road on such a night as this? Three times I doubted, but the flame repeated its signal a fourth time: someone is coming. And yet I thought I was totally unknown. We must make ready to receive him. Come then, last flame of Israel! For the approaching stranger, let us stir up one last expiring glimmer. And then let the curtain fall, raised for the last time, and let the half-opened lips of the dead shut down on their secret for ever, for ever! Ah! Ah! Ah! He draws near.

(*At this moment the Witch is on her knees, bending over the cauldron from which clouds of smoke seem to be rising. She shakes her head and body and her speech becomes more and more breathless and excited. She seems to be seeing in the water of the cauldron, as in a mirror, every thing she describes in her monologue*)

He is drawing nearer—the stranger—and yet he knows the way—he hasn't even a torch in his hand. I feel I am weighed down by the fatigue of his climb up the mountain! Ah! his climb; he keeps slipping on the wet path— of the mountain; the wind blows—it whistles through his cloak. Oh! the fatigue. I feel I am on the point of death already! Wretched woman, as old as the cares of the world and who only wants to die in peace . . . He is drawing near—nearer—the stranger. Ah! the brambles are tearing him! Bareheaded; he looks as mortally tired, ah! as my miserable self. He falls on his knees. Praying! No, he is getting up. He is running now—running up the path to my cave; he holds a javelin in his hand— mercy on me! I have no strength; I hear his steps; he is here! here!

(*The Witch, more and more haggard, lifts her head. When she says "Here!" she looks round with a glance that shows that her two fields of vision—the imaginary and the real— have become one*)

Am I going to die?

(*Her voice, louder and louder and with a scream*)

Mercy on me! Mercy! Mercy! *Saul!!!*

(*Saul stands on the threshold. A torn cloak of rough woollen
stuff covers him; he looks haggard; his hair dripping with
rain is blown over his forehead*)

SAUL (*in a heart-broken voice*)

Oh! you recognise me? But I don't look like a king,
do I?

WITCH (*her face on the ground*)

Have mercy, Saul. Mercy on me, wretched that I am.

SAUL

Am I less wretched than you?

WITCH

Have mercy, Saul! on me who am about to die.

SAUL

Don't be afraid of me, Pythoness! I have not come to
judge you. I have come to implore you. I don't want you
to implore *me*.

(*He takes his head in his hands*)

My distress is unbearable.

WITCH

Is it King Saul who speaks so?

SAUL

Yes. It is Saul. Not the King. Oh! why, why, Pythoness,
did you foretell me royalty? Do you remember how handsome I was with no crown? The least shepherd of the

hills—I was one of them—has more royalty in his bearing than my crown and purple robes have given me.
I know one, who, as he makes his way, is more than
glorious . . . As for me . . . (*He drops sitting on a stone.*)
I am tired.

WITCH (*rising*)

Saul! (*In a condoling voice, and not knowing what to say.*)
In this weather, the way was hard.

SAUL

The weather? Was it raining?

(*He fingers his dripping cloak*)

Yes. I am cold. Come nearer. I am in need of consolation.

WITCH (*touching Saul's forehead very tenderly*)

Saul!

SAUL

What?

WITCH

Nothing. I pity you, King Saul.

SAUL

Ah! Pity? It's true that I'm pitiable, Pythoness! For
nights now I have . . .

(*He seems to be swaying in his seat*)

Oh! I am fainting. For nights and nights I have been searching and wearing out my soul with searching.

WITCH

Searching for what? The future, Saul?

SAUL (*with the air of a prophet*)

Incomparable torments of my soul! (*Recovering himself.*) I'm not always as weak as this; on certain days I still seem quite reasonable; but the way here exhausted me. I wouldn't eat anything this evening.

WITCH

I have a few morsels of bread. Will you have some?

SAUL

No; not yet; my soul is hungrier than my body. But tell me, Pythoness, can you call up the dead?

WITCH (*distressed*)

The dead, you want? But whom?

SAUL

Whom? Samuel.

WITCH (*terrified*)

He is too great.

SAUL

Am I Saul?

WITCH

Then be obeyed. You are still master.

(She goes up to the hearth and makes signs and gestures of a kind to call up the dead)

Look! The flame has begun to flare already. Stand away.

SAUL *(standing upright, holds his cloak in front of his face, so that the apparition may be hidden from him, but not from the audience)*

Samuel! Samuel! Samuel! It is I. I call upon your awful apparition in fear. Speak to me! Let one word of yours shatter or save me! My uncertainty has become intolerable; and my anxiety is harder to bear than any word of yours.

Pythoness! Pythoness! What do you see?

WITCH

Nothing so far.

SAUL

I dare not look. The soul within me is light and leaping as though with a desire to sing. I am fainting. Pythoness! Pythoness! What do you see?

WITCH

Nothing. Ah! Ah! Ah! I see a God ascending from the earth.

SAUL

What is he like?

WITCH

An old man is coming up; he is wrapped in a mantle.

SAUL (*falling prostrate*)

Samuel!

SHADE OF SAMUEL

Why hast thou disturbed me in my sleep?

SAUL

I am in great distress. The Philistines make war against me, and the Lord has departed from me.

SHADE OF SAMUEL

Why dost thou consult me, since the Lord God has withdrawn from thee and become thy enemy?

SAUL

Whom can I consult but thee? For the Lord no longer answers me, nor the prophets, nor dreams. Who will make known to me what I should do?

SHADE OF SAMUEL

Saul, Saul, why dost thou always lie in the face of thy Lord? Thou knowest that from the depths of thy heart another thought arises. It is not the Philistines that disquiet thee, and it is not for that that thou hast come to question me.

SAUL

Speak then, Samuel. Thou who knowest my secret better than I myself. Fear has come upon me from every side. I dare not look upon my thought. What is it?

SHADE OF SAMUEL

Saul! Saul! Thou hast other enemies to overcome than the Philistines; but that which hurteth thee, thou dost harbour.

SAUL

I will overcome . . .

SHADE OF SAMUEL

Too late, Saul. It is now thine enemy that the Lord protects. Before he was conceived in his mother's womb, the Lord had already chosen him. It is to make ready for that that thou dost harbour him.

SAUL

But what then was my fault?

SHADE OF SAMUEL

To harbour him.

SAUL

But since God had chosen him.

SHADE OF SAMUEL

Dost thou think that God had not seen from afar the waverings of thy soul in order to punish thee for them? He placed thine enemies at thy door; thy chastisement is in their hands; they are waiting behind the door thou hast left ajar; but it was long ago that they were invited. In thy heart thou knowest too the impatience of that waiting; what thou callest fear, thou knowest is in reality desire.

Hark! Those Philistines thou speakest of are already making ready. God will deliver all Israel into their hands.

(*Saul falls full length on the ground*)

For thee, thy royalty will become as a purple robe that is being torn, or as water that slips through the open fingers of thy hand.

SAUL (*sighing*)

And Jonathan?

SHADE OF SAMUEL

Jonathan will not have a drop left to drink, nor a shred of purple to cover him. . . . Oh! Unhappy Saul! How wilt thou bear the future, when its forecast alone is so crushing?

SAUL

LORD GOD of Hosts! My future is in Thy Almighty hands.

(*He falls senseless*)

SHADE OF SAMUEL

Yes, unhappy Saul! Thou who hast cut off the seers and made away with all who interpret dreams, dost thou think thou canst make away with the future? Hark! Thy future is already on the march, sword in hand. Thou canst cut off those who watch it approaching, but thou canst not prevent its approach. It is approaching, Saul, it is approaching! And it is already so near that thou canst no longer prevent anyone from seeing it.

Why, since thou art unable to hear me, didst thou ask me to come up? My word, now that it has been called forth, will go on; henceforward it will never cease from spreading; if now thou didst make an end of all prophets, things themselves would take a voice; and if thou didst refuse to listen to that, it is thyself that wouldst become a prophet.

In three days' time, the Philistines will attack and the flower of Israel will succumb. Look! the crown is no longer on thy head. God has placed it on David's . . . on David's. Look! Jonathan himself, with his own hands is placing it there. Farewell, Saul! Thou and thy son, you will soon join me again.

(*The Shade vanishes*)

WITCH (*faintly*)

And I yet sooner, Samuel!

(*Silence*)

SAUL (*as though waking up*)

I am hungry!

WITCH (*kneeling beside Saul, who is still lying on the ground*)

Saul!

SAUL (*partly raising himself*)

Yes, Saul. I am hungry. Come now, old woman. You must take pity on the King. You see he is ill. Give him something to eat.

WITCH

Poor Saul! I had kept these few morsels of bread.
Take them.

SAUL (*not yet come to himself*)

Tell me. Who was talking here just now? (*Agitated*)
Old woman, who was talking to you? Quick now! What
was it I came here to do? Make haste. Answer! Aren't
you the Witch of Endor? . . .

WITCH

Poor Saul!

SAUL

The Witch! No, no! All the sorcerers are dead! Saul
had them all killed. The Witch of Endor is dead . . .
(*raising himself*) or is going to die.

WITCH (*still kneeling*)

Ah! you needn't strike her, Saul. She'll soon die without that. Let her be.

SAUL (*completely himself again and getting more and more excited*)

Who was talking to you? Wasn't it . . . Who allowed
you to call up Samuel?

WITCH

Unhappy man!

SAUL

Ah! I will blot out all that he said. . . . I will blot it
out in your ears! I myself have almost forgotten it.

WITCH

Unhappy man!

SAUL

But . . . I didn't hear everything . . . (*Turning furiously on the witch*) Oh! wretch that you are! But you *shall* speak! I remember it all now! I fainted . . . What did he say? What did he say? What did he say?

WITCH

Unhappy man!

SAUL

Ah! Ah! You *shall* speak, Witch! Did he name? Tell me . . . did he . . . name anyone?

WITCH

Mercy!

SAUL

Anyone . . . else . . . ?

WITCH

Mercy, Saul!

SAUL

Besides me?

WITCH

Mercy on me!

SAUL

And Jonathan—as . . .

244

WITCH

No.

SAUL

Come, you know it all now, as my successor to the
throne?

WITCH

No!

SAUL

Liar! Liar! . . . Did someone tell you that I loved . . .

WITCH

Saul!

SAUL

Yes? . . . You know . . . you know . . . David?

WITCH

Why have you named him?

SAUL

No! No! Don't say it! No! No!

(*He strikes the Witch with his javelin*)

WITCH

You have wounded me!

SAUL

No! No! Come now! It was just a touch of my javelin;
speak! Go on! Say it wasn't he!

WITCH (*leaning on her arm and Saul bending over her*)

Saul! You have wounded me mortally. Saul! I was
going to die! Why didn't you let me be? Look, my pale
blood is running over your cloak!

SAUL

No! No! I haven't hurt you. Come now, speak! You
can surely put off dying for a moment. (*Imploring*) Ah,
answer, I beseech you!

WITCH

Let my soul, ah! fall asleep—quietly—it is at peace.

SAUL

No, not yet.

WITCH

King Saul!

SAUL

What?

WITCH

King so deplorably given to welcoming, shut your
door!

SAUL

Ah, answer me: did he name?

WITCH

Let my soul gently fall asleep.

SAUL (*taking his head in his hands*)

Ah! . . .

WITCH

King Saul!

SAUL (*with a last gleam of hope*)

What?

WITCH (*in the throes of death*)

Shut your door!! Close your eyes! Stop your ears, and let not love's perfume . . .

SAUL (*with a start of fear*)

What?

WITCH (*with an effort*)

. . . find a way into your heart. All that is delightful to you is your enemy. Free yourself! Saul! . . . Saul! . . .

(*She dies*)

SAUL (*leaning over her more and more as her voice grows weaker, and as if he was still waiting for a further revelation*)

What? She is dead.

*(He looks round him. The fire has gone out. The cave
has become very dark)*

Am I henceforth to grope alone for ever in the dark?

(He makes his way out, groping)

SCENE IV

*The large hall of the 1st Act. The curtains on both sides
are closely drawn. Saul is seated on his throne in regal state—
purple robe, crown and lance. David, sitting beside him on a
stool, or simply on the ground, is playing the harp before
the King.*

DAVID *(singing)*

*. . . Around thee pious men give praise.
The King's enemies are put to flight.
The Lord God defendeth the King.*

(Pause)

And here is a new song I have invented for Saul:

*Words full of sweetness! gush forth! overflow from my heart!
I sing. My song is for the King.
May it be like the song of a skilful writer!*

(Pause)

*Awake, my lute!
Awake my lute and my harp!
Let my song waken the dawn!*

(Pause)

King Saul! Mount on thy chariot!
Defend truth and mercy and justice!
Mount on thy chariot, King Saul!

(*Pause*)

All thy warriors await thee . . .
The Philistines rejoice in their waiting;
Saul sleepeth; Saul appeareth not.

(*Pause*)

Mount thy chariot, great King!
Let not God's enemies triumph!
Let them not rejoice!

(*Pause*)

Saul! Saul! Awaken!
My sounding lute is thy companion.
Thy right hand shineth with great deeds.

(*Pause*)

Valiant warrior! Gird thy sword!
Put on thy apparel and thy glory!
Yes! Yes! Thy glory!

(*Saul, slightly bored, begins to yawn, and then signs to*
David to stop)

SAUL

Don't you know anything rather more cheerful?

DAVID

More cheerful?

SAUL

Yes. Are you surprised? You don't know me well enough. There! Put aside your harp, David! Let's talk. We must pass the time pleasantly. Tell me! What am I like, David?

DAVID

Like a king.

SAUL

No. You don't understand. I mean, what do you think the most remarkable thing about me?

DAVID

Your royalty.

SAUL (*irritated*)

Ah! (*Thinking better of it*) Even without my beard?

DAVID

A little less without your beard.

SAUL

It's because I'm easier to see that I look less like a king. Yes. That's why I had my beard shaved. I felt less like a king than I looked. While now . . . tell me you like me better so.

DAVID

I like the King better.

SAUL

No, David. I look younger to you now—and so I am. Because it made me look older in your eyes, I didn't like that royal beard . . . It was for you I had it cut . . . David . . .

(*David, embarrassed, begins playing the harp again. Saul, furious, is on the point of striking him*)

David!

(*David makes a movement*)

Don't go away! I was only joking. I mean . . . Let's talk a little more, David. Tell me, do you sometimes pray to God?

DAVID

Yes, King Saul. Often.

SAUL

Why? He never grants one's prayers.

DAVID

What can the King pray for that is never granted? What can a King pray for?

SAUL (*hesitating and then abruptly*)

And you? What do you pray for?

DAVID (*in some confusion*)

Never to become king.

SAUL (*in a rage leaps down from his throne upon David, who remains motionless, then, leaning over him, whispers in his ear*)

David! David! Shall we combine together against God? David, supposing it was I who gave you the crown?

(*Saul gazes at David and then, disturbed by his astonishment and fright, resorts to a burst of laughter*)

Ha! Ha! Ha! You see that a beardless king is still able to laugh.

(*He goes back to his throne and sits down. Then, angrily*)

That's enough. I won't be the only one to laugh. By the Lord God! I really believe you thought I was in earnest. The crown! David! You want the crown! Ha! Ha! Fie! And Jonathan? Have you forgotten poor, dear Jonathan?

(*David, at the end of his tether, makes a move to go away*)

Oh! there he is now wanting to go off! Wild bird! Can nothing tame you? Sing then! . . . Come, David! Something gay!

(*David makes a gesture*)

No? Nothing gay? You know nothing gay? What! do you never joke, David? Not with your Jonathan? Never!! Well then! Just play! For that matter, your singing disturbs my thoughts. One can't always be entertained.

(*David begins to play on the harp and goes on playing till the end of the scene*)

Ah! Ah! This singing of the harp flows over my thoughts . . . I too once praised the Lord, David! I sang songs to Him; there was a time when my mouth was always open in His praise, and my tongue never ceased to speak in His honour. But my lips now are afraid to open and are closed down over my secret; and my secret, alive within me, cries aloud with all its strength.

(Saul, getting more and more excited, begins to speak as though in delirium)

Silence is wearing me away. Since I have stopped speaking, my soul is being consumed; its secret is eating it away day and night like an ever wakeful fire.

(He stops for a moment during a slight pause of the music)

Horror! Horror! Horror! They want to know my secret and I don't know it myself! It is slowly growing in my heart . . . But the music stirs it . . . Like a bird beating at the bars of its cage, it rises to my teeth; it leaps to my lips, it leaps in longing to rush out . . . ! David! my soul is in unparalleled torments! . . . My lips, what name are you uttering? Shut tight, oh! lips of Saul! Wrap close your royal mantle, Saul! You are besieged by all that lies around you! Stop your ears against his voice! All that comes near me is hostile to me! Shut down, gates of my eyes! All deliciousness is hostile! Delicious! Delicious! Oh! to be with him, a goatherd like him, beside the running brooks! Oh! to see him all day long! To wander with him in the ardour of the desert, as once, alas! long ago, seeking for my she-asses. In the heat of the air, I should burn! And then I should feel my soul less burning—my soul which this music stirs—and which rushes from my lips—towards you, Daoud, delicious.

(David flings his harp on the ground, so that it breaks. Saul seems to be waking out of a dream)

SAUL

Where am I?
David! David! Stop! Stop!

DAVID

Farewell, Saul! No longer for you alone will your secret be intolerable!

(*He goes out*)

ACT IV

Night time, but not very dark. The scene is laid in a narrow strip of garden, where a hill-side ends abruptly. On the left a spring bubbles out; cypress trees are set regularly round it. Jonathan and Saki.

JONATHAN

Are you sure this is the right place? Yes. Here are the spring and the cypresses.—Ah! Saki, how beautiful the night is in this garden. Oh! if I had only known of it sooner, I should have come here often. And how does one get up to this plateau?

SAKI

Oh! one has to go a long way round.

JONATHAN

Ah! Ah! There it is!

SAKI

What, Prince? What are you looking for?

JONATHAN

A bird, my boy. That's why I've brought my bow; I have been told that every night it flies over this spring and settles over there! There! Don't you see it?

SAKI

No.

JONATHAN

Look! Look at the way it's flying! It's wheeling round
. . . and round . . . as if it were going to settle!

SAKI

But I can't see anything at all!

JONATHAN

There! It has dropped. There! Can't you really see
anything? Near that white stone! Over there! Now mark
where my arrow is going . . . Got him! Run along!
Quick! Quick! Bring me back the bird or my arrow.

(*As soon as Saki has disappeared, David comes out from
behind a bush*)

DAVID

Jonathan!

JONATHAN

Oh David! I thought I was going to die of fright!
Make haste! There's hardly a minute to spare! Saki will
be back in no time! But why in this garden? Wouldn't
it have been easier to meet in the palace?

DAVID

No, Jonathan. No one must know I am here. I am
going now. To-night I must say good-bye to you.

JONATHAN

Oh, Daoud! What! Good-bye! Going away!

(*He sinks down, overcome, beside the spring*)

DAVID

Oh, Jonathan! I haven't enough strength of my own to leave you; I must have yours too. Don't give way! Pull yourself together!

JONATHAN

Away from you, no pleasure is left me . . . Going away?

DAVID (*hesitating*)

I must . . . Saul . . .

JONATHAN

Tell me . . . My father . . .

DAVID

He can't endure my presence any longer. He . . .

JONATHAN

He struck you?

DAVID

Yes . . . struck! struck! You know how irritable he is. Oh! Jonathan! bear up! I shall see you again, Jonathan.

JONATHAN

Where are you going? With you away, I have no strength left. . . .

DAVID (*hesitating at first*)

Where am I going? . . . now? To the Philistines.

JONATHAN

The Philistines!!

DAVID

Make haste and understand me. Saki will be back in a moment. I don't want him to catch sight of me. If your father were to hear . . . But the urgent thing is this. Listen! The Philistines are making ready again. Your father is uneasy; I don't know what is troubling him, but his heart and soul are not ready for battle; and if the Philistines attack now, he will assuredly be beaten. The Philistines are going to attack; that is certain, and that is why I, myself, want to be at their head . . . It will look as if I were marching against you, but, if I take the crown away from Saul, it will be to give it back again to you.

JONATHAN (*as if he had heard nothing*)

The Philistines! Daoud! You with the Philistines!

DAVID

Oh! try to understand! Never, if I thought there was any hope of your father's being victorious; but you know that something is devouring him; nothing can distract him from it—and this disturbance of his soul is reflected in his army. His soldiers have become restless. He is incapable of taking their lead.

JONATHAN

And I?

DAVID

You, Jonathan? Alas! You would both succumb. Oh!
Let me be victorious for you as well. But listen and pay
attention to what I am saying. If, on the evening of the
second day, you see the enemy's army encamped on the
hill—the one opposite the town—the hill of Gilboa, fear
nothing; this is what you must do . . .

JONATHAN

Go on. I will do as you tell me.

DAVID

At the end of the garden, hidden among lemon trees
and brambles, there is the opening of a very large cave;
I shall be waiting there the whole night. Don't be afraid.
I think no one knows the way in. Come without a torch,
so that you mayn't be seen. The sky is clear and the
moon is full. It's a kind of cave, half open from above,
so that one can see the sky once one has got over the
first difficulties. I shall be expecting you; I will guide
you through the dark. We shall be able to talk. We shall
plan what we must. . . .

(*Saki is heard singing*)

JONATHAN

What? Oh! tell me!

DAVID

Saki is coming. Jonathan, my brother! My soul is sobbing with love . . . Good-bye! Remember!

(*He looks back as he goes off*)

More than my soul . . . Ah! Jonathan! more than
my soul.

JONATHAN

Enough! David—enough! or you will take my life with you.

(*Enter Saki*)

SAKI

Prince! the bird had flown away. I could only find the arrow.

JONATHAN

Come!

(*Exeunt Saki and Jonathan*)

SCENE II

A desert. An arid and sandy plain, slightly hillocky. A blazing sun. Left, a Demon lies stretched on a hillock wrapped in an enormous brown cloak, which drags out at length over the sand.

Saul enters right, bare-headed, a knotty stick in his hand. He is not wearing his royal cloak, but only his undergarments.

SAUL

Let's be careful! It's in a sun like this that the wisdom of kings evaporates. What did I come here to look for? Ah! My asses! . . . All traces disappear here, like water in the sand.

(*He bends down to look at the ground, and then starts back*)

Ugh! A snake!

DEMON (*without stirring*)

Won't harm you.

SAUL (*not greatly surprised*)

What?

DEMON

I said it wouldn't harm *you*, at any rate. . . . Oh, really!
You can't pretend you're afraid of serpents now, old
King!

SAUL

This little rascal shows little respect for me.

(*Goes forward to beat him*)

DEMON

It must be granted, King Saul, that without your beard
you no longer look so very respectable.

(*The King strikes him, and prods him with his stick*)

Oh! no! no! Don't tickle me! I shall die of laughter!

(*He shakes with laughter. The King too*)

King Saul, where have you left your crown? Was it
with David?

SAUL (*putting his hand to his head*)

I jumped about a little in the desert. It must have
fallen off.

DEMON

Take care of the sun in the desert; you haven't got enough hair now to go about like that without your crown. Take my hat.

(*He passes him his bonnet, which the King puts on*)

King Saul! where have you left your cloak? Your fine purple cloak, King Saul? Was it with David?

SAUL

I was too hot . . . It's very hot in the desert.

DEMON

But at night it's very cold in the desert. Take my cape.

SAUL

And you?

DEMON

I'm accustomed to the desert.

SAUL (*stripping him of his cape*)

Hullo! You never told me you were so handsome.

DEMON (*naked*)

A bit black, perhaps!

SAUL

No! No!

DEMON

A matter of taste.

(*Saul has put on the enormous cloak which trails behind him*)

And where did you leave your sceptre, eh?

SAUL (*automatically*)

With David. It was too heavy. This stick is better suited to the desert.

DEMON (*holding out his hand*)

Show me! But King Saul, it's a serpent!

SAUL

Little silly! (*He laughs*) A serpent! a serpent! No, no! None of your nonsense!

(*The stick turns into a serpent and glides away*)

I'll be after you!

(*The King goes down on all fours*)

DEMON (*standing upright on the hillock*)

It must be granted you don't look much of a king like that. (*He laughs*) Do you know what made me recognise you, Saul?

(*Saul comes back*)

Your beauty!

SAUL (*admirable in his great cloak—anxiously*)

No? Really? I still look . . . ?

DEMON

I haven't seen you look like that for many a long year!
My young Saul! You've been here already, do you remember? You were looking for some asses.

SAUL (*sighing*)

Ah! my she-asses!

DEMON

King Saul, where did you leave your she-asses?

SAUL

Do you know where, eh? Do *you* know?

DEMON (*pulling him by his cloak*)

Come on then! We'll look for them together, shall we?
(*They go off behind the sandhill. The Demon's voice is heard*)
Oh, King Saul, I'm so tired! Carry me.

SAUL (*in a caressing voice, off*)

Poor little thing! Poor little thing!

SCENE III

*The Palace hall as in Act I. A crowd of people pushing to
see the King when he comes in, but they leave a passage from
the entrance on the right to the throne. On the right side the
Barber and Johel are watching the crowd and talking in a low
voice. Most of the others have their backs turned to the audience.*

1ST MAN

And then?

2ND MAN

Then they brought him back to the palace.

1ST MAN

Was he still singing?

2ND MAN

I should just think he was! Singing and dancing too! There was no stopping him.

3RD MAN

The Prince gave orders that he should have his robes put on him, and his crown; but he danced about so much that it wouldn't stop on his head.

(*They laugh*)

4TH MAN

It's vexing all the same! For once that one chooses one's own King . . .

5TH MAN

David chose himself.

3RD MAN

But they say he doesn't want to be King.

5TH MAN

My foot! Is there anyone who doesn't want to be King?

2ND MAN

Would you like it? You?

1ST MAN

And what would you do if you were King?

5TH MAN

I should begin by chucking out David.

(*They laugh*)

6TH MAN (*coming up angrily*)

Who's speaking ill of David?

3RD, 4TH AND 5TH MEN

No one is speaking ill of David.

6TH MAN

Just you wait till he comes back and you'll soon see whether it's he will be chucked out—or Saul.

SEVERAL (*with an air of implying they don't think much of him*)

Oh, Saul! . . . Saul!

(*An old Jew coming up and questioning the 2nd Man*)

OLD JEW

And what did Saul say?

2ND MAN

Who knows? He shouted something or other.

3RD MAN

He himself doesn't know what he's saying.

OLD JEW

One must always listen to the prophets.

4TH AND 5TH MEN

But Saul isn't a prophet.

(*More and more people come up*)

7TH MAN

Yes! Yes! Saul's a prophet. I was there when he danced before Samuel.

8TH MAN

Is it true that Samuel blessed David before dying?

A CHILD

Is it true that King Saul has had his beard shaved off?

(*All laugh. Others come up. The conversation starts in another place*)

9TH, 2ND AND 3RD MEN

Yes. Yes. It's true!

1ST MAN AND OTHERS

What rubbish!
Nonsense!
What! His whole beard?

10TH MAN

I don't think that's right, a King without a beard!

4TH MAN

But David hasn't got a beard.

10TH MAN

David hasn't got a beard *yet* . . .

5TH MAN

And then David's handsome.

4TH MAN (*to the* 10*th*)

And what about Jonathan?

SEVERAL

Oh! Jonathan! When *he* gets one!

OTHERS (*right*)

Hush! Hush! Here's the King!

ONE MAN (*very loud*)

Why "Hush"?

(*Murmurs in the crowd*)

It's true! True! He's shaved his beard!

1ST MAN (*to the people round him*)

Don't shout like that!

ANOTHER MAN (*to the* 1*st*)

Oh! for the last day or two he doesn't hear anything that's said to him.

ANOTHER

It's true he looks ill.

6TH MAN

And what about Jonathan, then?

5TH MAN AND OTHERS

Oh! As for him!

ANOTHER (*some way off*)

Don't push so!

CHILD

Jacob! Jacob! Lift me up. I want to see a King without a beard.

(*All laugh. The crowd divide on each side of the throne in such a way that the audience may see the King approaching. But at first it is obvious that the crowd see him before the actors*)

1ST MAN

Why does he come in alone like that? I thought he always had guards with him.

3RD MAN

Oh! Not now! No one pays any attention to him. When he calls, everyone goes away.

(Saul comes in, hesitating as if he were drunk, or rather, as if he were aware of a hostile and jeering crowd about him. He has the expression of a madman—sometimes full of hatred, sometimes of fear; he is leaning on Jonathan, whose strength seems failing. His shamefaced, sad expression seems to be imploring the people.

On hearing the last words, Saul brandishes his javelin absurdly; a slight movement of recoil among the crowd)

3RD MAN

No need to be frightened. His javelin hasn't got a point.

1ST MAN

Is it true they won't allow him any weapons now?

2ND MAN

They're jolly well right.

5TH MAN

They say he tried to kill David.

(Jonathan is obviously pained by all this talk. Just then someone in the crowd throws a rotten fruit at Saul which squashes on his back)

SOMEONE (*furiously*)

One for you!

(Others turn round indignantly. Scuffle. Noise. The King mounts the throne; Jonathan stands beside him, his head in his hands. Saul makes gestures as if wishing to speak. In the crowd cries of—)

Silence! Silence!

SAUL (*standing*)

Dear Hebrews!

(*Laughter in the crowd*)

SOME

What did he say? What did he say?

SAUL

Dear Hebrew people!

(*More and more laughter. The King is visibly perturbed. He speaks slowly, finding his words with difficulty*)

On the eve of an important battle . . .

(*His voice is completely drowned by an increasing noise coming from the left; the people shove and are seen to be questioning fresh arrivals; a few words are heard coming from the crowd*)

Yes, on the Hill of Gilboa!

OTHER VOICES

What? What?
David's army . . . Philistines . . . Yes. One can see them from the market place. . . .
Where? Where?

(*A loud voice is heard above all the others crying solemnly*)

King Saul! David's army is encamped on Mount Gilboa!

ALL

Let's go and see! Go and see!

(*Tumult. They all rush off in confusion*)

SOME LITTLE GIRLS

Quick! Quick!

(*Jonathan raises his head as if waking out of a dream; he looks round him; looks at Saul and murmurs*)

JONATHAN

The evening of the second day! Ah! David! David!

(*He darts off, transported by joy or anxiety, in the opposite direction from the crowd*)

SAUL (*shouting like an angry schoolmaster to his unruly boys*)

Stop there! You're to stop! Do you hear? I tell you to stop!

(*He starts running after them; then throws his javelin clumsily; then goes lamentably to pick it up. The stage is now empty. On the steps of the throne a small boy, Saki, sits sobbing. The King comes back*)

SAUL (*catching sight of him*)

You, Saki? (*Very tenderly*) Is it because of me you're crying? . . . Poor Saki!

(*Saki goes on crying. The King is embarrassed, and hesitates between his sentences*)

You mustn't be sorry for me. So you're fond of me, Saki?

SAKI (*sobbing*)

They've all left you, all left you.

SAUL

And that's why you're crying, little Saki? But you know, it isn't serious. (*Aside*) Oh! I wish I could comfort the poor little thing! So you love me a little, Saki?

SAKI

Oh! A great deal! A great deal!

SAUL

Really? And why?

SAKI

You're good to me.

SAUL

I? Good?

SAKI

Yes; on the terrace you used to make me drink . . .

SAUL (*disgusted with himself*)

Ah! Wine!

SAKI

And then . . . and then . . .

SAUL

Well?

SAKI

You're alone.

273

SAUL (*unexpectedly moved*)

No, no, my little Saki. You see I'm not. *You* are with me. Oh! I didn't know anyone was sorry for me. What am I to do?

(*Enter several officers, preceded by the High Priest, in great agitation*)

HIGH PRIEST (*as if he had something very important to say*)
King Saul——

SAUL (*interrupting him*)

Leave me alone. Can't you see that I'm busy?

(*They all go out, giving it up as a bad job*)

SAUL (*to Saki*)
Would it amuse you to be a King, Saki?

SAKI

Oh! No!

SAUL

What! You wouldn't like to be the King?

SAKI

I don't know.

SAUL

"I don't know!" Come along! Will you try on my crown?

(*He takes the crown and approaches it to Saki's head*)

274

SAKI (*pushing it away*)

No!

SAUL (*giving up for the moment*)

Tell me, Saki, why didn't you follow David?

SAKI

I don't know.

SAUL (*more and more irritated*)

"I don't know!" Then you're not fond of David?

SAKI

Oh, yes! But . . .

SAUL

But?

SAKI

I like being with you better.

SAUL

But I thought, Saki, that you left me to be with Jonathan. These last few nights on the terrace, you left me . . .

SAKI

For Jonathan, yes.

SAUL

Well! David and Jonathan . . . they go together, don't they?

SAKI

Often, yes.

SAUL

And they're more amusing than an old king.

SAKI

Oh! You're not old, King Saul!

SAUL (*he has not put his crown on again, but keeps it on his knees and from time to time makes as though he were going to put it on Saki's head, but takes it back whenever Saki, who is sitting at his feet, raises his head*)

Really? You think I am still amusing?

SAKI

David and Jonathan aren't amusing.

SAUL

Ah! And what do they do?

SAKI

Nothing.

SAUL

Ah! And what do they say?

SAKI

Nothing.

SAUL

Do they talk?

SAKI

Yes.

SAUL

And what do they say?

SAKI

I don't know.

(*He drops his head lower out of embarrassment, so that Saul suddenly thrusts the crown on to his head. It comes down over his eyes*)

SAUL (*with forced playfulness*)

Ah! You don't know! . . . Peep-bo!! The crown!

SAKI (*terrified*)

Oh! What's that?

SAUL

It's the crown.

SAKI

It's come over my eyes! I can't see!

SAUL (*bursts out laughing*)

"I can't see!" Ha! Ha! Ha! Ha!

SAKI

It's hurting me dreadfully. Oh! take it off, King Saul!

SAUL (*pushing it down still further with both hands*)

What does David say?

SAKI (*sobbing*)

Nothing, I assure you! Oh, take it off!

SAUL (*rapping Saki's knuckles as he struggles to remove
the crown*)

Leave it alone! Leave it alone! It's just for fun. And
what does Jonathan say?

SAKI

Nothing, King Saul. I swear it.

SAUL

"Nothing, nothing!" And what else?

SAKI

He calls him "Daoud".

SAUL

I knew it! And then?

SAKI (*in despair*)

Nothing! Nothing! Nothing! King Saul!

(*Saul with an air of tragedy takes off the crown*)

SAKI (*his hand to his forehead*)

Look! I'm bleeding!

SAUL (*almost triumphantly*)

Ha! You see! I'm not good!

(*Then abruptly, bending over Saki with great tenderness*)

Have I hurt you, Saki?

278

*(Saki, still terrified, frees himself from Saul, gets up
and goes out slowly, walking backwards)*

And what did they say when they caught me? That I
was mad? Tell me! *(Confidentially)* Tell me, did you know
I had run away? Tell me! But now they won't let me go
without my crown. . . . It's Jonathan who wants . . .

(Noticing just then that Saki is going off, says very sadly)

Oh! Saki! You're going away? And you said you loved
me, Saki!

*(Saki, touched, returns and stands close to the King.
Saul bends down and says confidentially)*

Hark! My she-asses! You know, my she-asses! Well
I know where they are!! Will you come too? We'll go
and fetch them together! We'll escape! . . . We'll escape!

(They go out)

SCENE III

*A cave, or rather a cavern. Left, the vaulted top has fallen
in, allowing the light of the full moon to shine through a tangle
of shrubs and creepers. Stones and boulders lie on the ground.
On the right, the further end of the cave is very dark. A steep
path leads down in the background, by which Saul comes,
feeling his way step by step.*

SAUL

Hullo! A spring! It's very slippery. I nearly fell down.
It's wet underfoot. Where are you bringing me?

(The Demon, becoming visible, remains silent)

279

SAUL

Is this the place? Come on, answer! It's always the same thing! You needn't think you can make me go wherever you please only to find nothing I was looking for.

(Going forward towards the left)

Dear me! It's rather curious here! Not a bad place for a little talk . . . In reality, you know, I'm not as keen as all that on finding my she-asses. Only, really, at my age you make me walk too far. I may get tired, you know.

(After looking for a place where to sit down, he chooses a kind of natural bench in the dark part of the cave and sits down. To the Demon)

Sit there! *(Pointing vaguely in front of him.)* No! don't sit on the ground. It's too wet!

(He passes him his crown)

Sit on that.

(The Demon sits on it)

First of all, kindly tell me . . .

(He sneezes as if he had caught cold)

Because if it's not for my she-asses, why have you brought me here?

(He sneezes)

DEMON

Bless you!

SAUL

You said?

DEMON (*laughing*)

He! He! He!

SAUL

Ah! I don't like people laughing when I'm not in a laughing mood.

DEMON

Oh, King Saul! It's so funny! Do you know who you're going to see here?

SAUL

Ah! Saki! If you only knew how little inclined I feel to laugh just now! Come on then! Who is it we're going to see?

(*He gets up as if to go towards the Demon*)

DEMON

Hush! Hush! Just listen!

(*Sounds of steps and voices coming from the left*)

SAUL

Ah! Jonathan!

DEMON

And . . . ?

SAUL (*in a whisper*)

David!

DEMON

Say thank you!

DAVID (*as he appears with Jonathan in the moonlight on the left*)

Three times! Three times I shall have the trumpet sounded! As soon as you hear the first, you must get ready. It will be just before dawn. . . . Persuade Saul. At the third, I shan't be able to answer for anything any more. Before daybreak you must have taken refuge here, both of you.

SAUL (*makes as though to go towards them. The Demon pulls him back by his cloak*)

Oh! Oh! It's treason he's counselling!

DEMON

If you show yourself, they'll be off.

JONATHAN

Farewell, David.

DAVID (*putting his forehead on Jonathan's shoulder*)

Ah! Jonathan!

DEMON (*pulling Saul back*)

Come! Come! Now! Let's lie down. Let them get nearer. Pretend to be asleep. You'll see them better.

(*Saul lies down where he had at first been sitting. The Demon disappears*)

DAVID (*raising his head*)

Farewell. Go now. Leave me alone for a little. I want to pray.

JONATHAN

And what do you ask of God?

DAVID

Don't you know, Jonathan? To take away this crown from me.

SAUL (*mocking, aside*)

Simple, isn't it?

DEMON

Hush!

JONATHAN

Good-bye!

(*David kneels down among the rocks, almost turning his back to the audience. Jonathan moves towards the right, sees Saul and returns precipitately to David*)

David! David! My father's here.

(*David, absorbed in his prayers, does not stir*)

JONATHAN (*wildly*)

My father's here, David.

DAVID (*still praying*)

I haven't finished my prayers. Leave me!

JONATHAN (*draws aside again and looks towards Saul.*
To David)

He's asleep.

(*The moonlight, which, throughout the scene, has been slowly
moving towards the right, now falls on Saul's crown,
which is on the ground*)

Ah! His crown has rolled on the ground.

DAVID

I haven't done praying yet. Let me be!

(*Silence. Nothing stirs*)

SAUL

Isn't he going to come nearer?

(*David rises*)

JONATHAN

What are you going to do?

DAVID

Look.

(*He picks up the crown and puts it beside Saul's head*)

DAVID

You'll tell him, Jonathan. You must persuade him.

SAUL (*aside*)

I'm trembling. He'll understand. . . .

JONATHAN

He won't believe me.

DAVID (*coming back with a sudden idea*)

Ah!

(*He draws his sword, cuts off a large piece of purple cloth from the royal mantle and takes it away*)

Let him know it was I did it; and that when I cut off this piece of his cloak, I could have taken his life. Take care! He's waking up. Come, we must go!

(*They go out left*)

SAUL (*getting up, goes to where the moon is shining, and sees that his damaged cloak has left him almost indecently bare. Then sneeringly*)

How kind they are to me!

ACT V

It is night. The scene is laid in a vague and indistinct mountainous spot. On the right Saul's tent.

(Johel and the Barber in front of the tent)

BARBER

Still no orders?

JOHEL

Orders? Oh! yes, plenty of orders, but no directions.

BARBER

Is it true that the Hebrews are divided?

JOHEL

Divided? Not at all. They are all for David.

BARBER

The deuce they are! A funny kind of battle it'll be. And Saul? Is he for David too?

JOHEL (*more and more seriously*)

Be quiet, Barber! Saul is shaking like an old man. This fight will be merely a pretence battle. He has already accepted his defeat in his secret soul.

BARBER

Then what will you do, Johel?

JOHEL

And what will *you* do, Barber? Do you want my advice? Since when have I become your spiritual adviser? Get away. Here's Saul.

(*Enter Saul and Jonathan. The inside of the tent becomes visible, lighted with torches. Others enter, and with them Saki*)

SAUL (*to Jonathan*)

Look at my hands! See how they're trembling!

JONATHAN

Poor father!

SAUL

What do you think would do me most good? To drink some wine? Or not to drink it? I think to drink it. Go, Saki.

(*Exit Saki*)

To-day I shouldn't have the strength to kill anyone, not even an enemy. It is time for me now to draw near to God. (*Louder.*) Now leave me! The night is nearly over, and I must be alone in order to reflect.

(*Movement*)

You, Jonathan, stop. I have something more to say to you.

(*The rest go out. Saul paces up and down for some time without speaking*)

JONATHAN

Father, I have only a few moments.

SAUL (*sneezes*)

Draw that curtain. (*Sneezes again.*) I caught cold the other day in a cave. By the way, you know it perhaps; it's not far from here. David, prowler as he is, must know it.

JONATHAN (*more and more uneasy at Saul's insistence*)

Please, Father, let's make haste. There's only this one night left between us and the battle. We must prepare or else sleep.

SAUL (*sententiously*)

We must prepare, my son. To-night my whole soul is preparing.

JONATHAN

Father, we must prepare for action. What did you want to speak to me about?

SAUL

About that very thing, Jonathan. When, in times gone by, I used to act, I didn't understand that. There is a time for action, and a time to repent of action. Understand, my son, that there are more important things for the soul than victorious battles.

JONATHAN

But when, Father, were you so taken up with action?

SAUL

I know, I know. I was above all taken up with desiring.
But the time has come, my child, for me to repent of
that too.

(*Jonathan, more and more desperate, begins to leave*)

SAUL

Oh! Are you going?

JONATHAN

Time is pressing! I have everything to see to. I will
come back in a moment, Father.

SAUL

Jonathan, Jonathan, when my heart is quaking, you
desert me? Can't you stop and talk to me for a moment?
My son! I am kinder than I used to be, truly.

JONATHAN

Alas! But here's Saki. Let me go, Father.

(*Saki has come in*)

SAUL (*to both Jonathan and Saki*)

Ah! Go away yourselves! I'm mad to look for support
from you! Saki, take away that wine. I had better not
drink it. Go away! Go away!

(*Jonathan begins to go out. Saki stays in a corner of the
tent, unnoticed*)

JONATHAN (*as he goes*)

Father! When I come back will you follow me?

SAUL

Perhaps. (*Calling him back*) One moment, Jonathan! Jonathan! Don't be unhappy. Come back in a minute— just a minute. I'll follow you. But let me pray now.

(*Exit Jonathan*)

SAUL (*believing himself alone*)

Ah! Ah! Let's reflect. What am I?

DEMON (*hidden outside*)

Saul!

SAUL (*going to the door*)

Jonathan? (*He looks round*) No. I am alone. (*Kneeling*) My God! What am I in your eyes . . .

DEMON (*hidden*)

Saul!

SAUL

. . . that you should overwhelm me with desires? Whatever I seek to lean on for support, it gives way. I have nothing solid in me. What I like best in him is his strength. (*His mind wandering*) How wonderful the grace and suppleness of his limbs! I have seen him coming down the mountain side. He moves by leaps and bounds . . . (*Haggard and weary*) Have done, my lips!

(*He rises*)

DEMON (*plaintively*)

Saul!

SAUL

I am distraught!

DEMON

Saul!

SAUL

Ha! Someone calling me.

(*He goes to the tent door*)

SAKI (*trying to prevent him from opening the door*)

Don't open, King Saul!

SAUL

What! Was it you, Saki? What are you doing there?

SAKI

I'm afraid for you.

SAUL

Did you call me just now?

SAKI

No.

SAUL

Ah! It was outside!

SAKI

No! Don't open. . . . It's all outside; the night is full of them.

DEMON

Saul!

SAKI

Don't open to him.

SAUL

Oh! you hard-hearted little thing! Don't you hear someone's calling me?

(*Saul goes out with a torch*)

DEMON (*still very pathetic*)

Saul!

SAUL (*going up to the Demon and bending over it tenderly*)

Poor little thing! How he's trembling! Is it from cold? But he's quite frozen, the poor child! Come!

(*He touches him*)

We shall be warmer inside. Come along! I'll warm you up.

(*The Demon does not stir*)

Oh! all the same, I can't carry you, little creature!

(*He lifts him*)

Oh! He's frightfully heavy!

(*He carries him*)

Saki's going off. Good riddance!

(Exit Saki)

But he has left the wine. You shall have a drink.

(He puts the Demon down)

Ouf! Come! Cuddle up in my cloak.

(He sits down)

DEMON *(half rolled up in the cloak)*

It's torn.

SAUL *(smiling)*

Yes; David has already taken a bit out of that side.

DEMON *(giggling)*

He! He! He!

SAUL

What's the matter?

DEMON

Nothing.

SAUL

Is it funny?

DEMON

Yes. I'm thirsty.

293

SAUL (*handing him the flagon*)

Drink. . . . Better now? There. Close up. Now, keep quiet! I've a great deal to think of.

JONATHAN (*from outside*)

Father!

SAUL (*ashamed*)

There now! Bother! Jonathan!
Don't come in. (*To the Demon.*) Hide!

JONATHAN

Father, come with me now; it's time.

SAUL (*very uneasy*)

All right! I'm getting up. Just a moment . . . Go on! I'll be with you.

(*The Demon shows himself. He looks at Jonathan with a grin*)

JONATHAN

Oh! What's that?

SAUL

Just a small child who was shivering with cold. I took him into my tent.

JONATHAN (*profoundly sad*)

Ah?

SAUL (*ashamed*)

Yes.

294

JONATHAN (*more and more desperate*)

Father! Let him go now! Come!

SAUL (*not stirring and looking imbecile*)

Yes.

JONATHAN

O Father! Father! Don't you care for me a little more than for that little creature?

SAUL (*almost sobbing*)

Stop, Jonathan! . . . Jonathan! I implore you! You don't know how difficult it is!

JONATHAN

What's difficult? Poor father! How wretched you look!

SAUL

Jonathan, you are too young to understand me: I feel I am becoming wonderful! My value lies in my complication. Listen! I'll tell you some secrets: you think I was asleep the other night . . . in the cave.

JONATHAN (*pretending not to understand*)

The cave?

SAUL

Yes—you know—when David——

JONATHAN

David?

SAUL (*irritated*)

Yes, David . . . when he was plotting my defeat with you . . . and cut off a bit of my cloak in order to teach you better how to betray me. Ha! Ha! you understand each other admirably. What attention you show me! You'll thank him for me! You'll thank him, eh? Jonathan?

(*The Demon chuckles*)

You'll thank him kindly for me. He thinks I've fallen terribly low!

(*A blast of trumpets*)

JONATHAN

Ah!

SAUL

Ah! the signal!

JONATHAN

Come, Father. Ah, for your own sake!

SAUL

Crying! Jonathan! Jonathan, my son! Tell me you understand at least that it hurts me—it hurts me to make you cry. And just listen to this proverb, my own invention:

(*As he accompanies Jonathan to the door of the tent, he says sententiously*)

What shall console a man for his degradation, if not that which degraded him?

(*Dismissing Jonathan*)

Be off! Quick! To the cave! Run! I'll be with you in a moment!

(*Groups of soldiers are seen and heard passing by.
Jonathan goes*)

SAUL (*forgetting the Demon*)

Oh! What am I waiting for now in order to get up and act? My will! My will! I call on it now like a lost sailor hailing a boat he sees disappearing in the distance —disappearing! disappearing! I take sides with everything against myself.

(*He catches sight of the Demon drinking*)

Come! Leave me alone now. Good-bye. . . . Go away. I'm in need of rest.

(*The Demon does not stir*)

DEMON

You'll never rest again, King Saul.

SAUL

Never rest again! Oh! what makes you say that?

DEMON

Because I shall never leave you again, King Saul.

SAUL

Never!

DEMON

Nevermore!

SAUL

What! Never leave me again! And why not?

DEMON

Because you have nursed me.

SAUL

Nursed you? Why, what have I done for you, little wretch? I merely let you have a piece of my cloak. You were shivering!

DEMON

Yes. But now I'm marvellously warmed up. Just feel me. My skin is burning!

SAUL

No! Let me be! I won't. . . . Go away. I beg you, take pity on me, as I took pity on you.

DEMON

Pity! Come now, Saul! You mustn't tell me that if you took me in, it wasn't because it wasn't a pleasure to you yourself. Eh? To hold me in the fold of your cloak? Eh? Saul! Saul! Come now! Saul, make me laugh a little. Why so sad? Have I done you any harm, eh? Why are you vexed with me?

SAUL (*trying to defend himself*)

I want to pray.

DEMON (*not hearing*)

And then, you know . . . if you wanted to take pity . . . I'm not alone; there are a great many others outside.

298

SAUL (*allured—in spite of himself*)

Ah! There are others? Where?

DEMON

Why, there, behind the door.

SAUL (*goes to the door of the tent and raises it. The Demons come hustling in*)

Oh! What a number there are! All right! In with you! —If I refused hospitality to a single one, I should be afraid it might be the most charming, or perhaps, the most wretched.

(*The door falls to—a confused ceaseless humming fills the tent. The Demons swarm*)

1ST DEMON (*to the others*)

The King said something so excessively funny just now!

(*He whispers in their ears. Great confusion. They all laugh. A second trumpet call is heard*)

SAUL

Ah! Ah! The night is over. We must make haste.

JONATHAN (*calling from outside*)

Father!

SAUL (*rushing to the entrance and spreading out his cloak in order to hide the scene inside*)

Don't come in!

JONATHAN (*desperately*)

Oh! Come!

SAUL (*earnestly*)

For the sake of David's God, fly, Jonathan! Quick! Run! I'm coming!

(*Jonathan goes. Soldiers come on to the stage more and more tumultuously. Noise outside.—Tumult of Demons in the tent.—The day dawns slowly.—But the inside of the tent is still lighted only by the torches*)

SAUL (*coming forward to the footlights and addressing the audience. His voice dominates everything*)

Before I go, I want to sum up in a few words.

(*The Demons get noisier and noisier*)

Be quiet, you noisy creatures! Can't you see I want to speak to the public?

(*Addressing the audience*)

With what shall a man console himself . . . ?

DEMONS

But you've said it already, you've said it already. Ah! Ha! Ha!

(*Noise. The Demons' growing clamour is regulated by an accompaniment of music*)

SAUL (*turning round towards and against the Demons*)

What's all this? If you want to take the front place, give us a show at any rate. Let's see what you can do!

*(The Demons scuffle. Noise in time to the music. Saul
watches long and gravely. Then in disgust)*

Far from pretty!

DEMONS

But, Saul, you haven't taught us anything.

SAUL

Stop it, then! Stop it!

*(Jostled about, he falls on his knees; making the best
of it, he says)*

I want to pray.

*(Noise off. Saul, still on his knees, is gradually pushed
back towards the door by the Demons' jostling)*

(Praying) Shall I find any remedy for my desire other
than its satisfaction?

(Pushed still further back)

I sum up! I sum up! *(Haggard)* Oh! little ones, take
care! Take care! You're not leaving me room enough!
(Lower) I am totally suppressed!

*(Daybreak. A third call of trumpets is heard. Saul, half re-
gaining his feet, tears down the tent curtain. The Demons
vanish in the flood of daylight. The music stops)*

SAUL *(very loud in the silence)*

It is too late! Here is the daylight!

*(He comes out of the tent towards the left, kneels or
crouches on the ground, his hands in the grass)*

Oh, how refreshing this coolness! Now is the hour when the goatherds lead their flocks out of their stables . . . The grass is washed with dew . . .

(*Johel has come in with other soldiers of David's army*)

JOHEL (*catching sight of Saul*)

What! He's praying!

SAUL (*too much absorbed to see them*)

I am tempted.

SOLDIER (*to the others*)

David's men! Hark! Go and tell the King that Saul is here—unarmed. Run! David doesn't want him to be killed.

(*They go off. Johel stays behind*)

SAUL (*still absorbed*)

. . . washed with dew . . .

(*Johel approaches the King from behind, draws himself up to full height, brandishing his sword*)

Oh! Oh! Oh! Most cowardly of temptations, attacking me from behind!

(*Johel strikes him; Saul falls. Johel snatches his crown and carries it to David, who comes in escorted by a number of soldiers. At an order from David, Johel is seized. General disturbance. Broad daylight*)

David

Unhappy! Unhappy! You there! Take away that man!
(*Pointing to Johel*) Kill him and give his dead body to
be devoured by the beasts of the field! Shame on him
who lifts his hand against the Lord's anointed! He
has made this crown fall upon my head with all its
weight.

(*He bends over Saul and, taking the crown which had at first
been placed by his orders beside Saul, he puts it on his
own head. Bending low and in a whisper*)

I didn't hate you, King Saul!

(*Standing upright again*)

And Jonathan too, you say! Unhappy! Unhappy! Let
him be brought here. Lay him beside Saul that they may
be united in death. What are those cries and lamentations?
Grief dwells in my heart.

(*A procession brings in Jonathan's body*)

Mountains of Gilboa! Let there nevermore be honey
or dew on your slopes!

(*Bending over Jonathan*)

I did what I could, Jonathan! I did what I could,
Jonathan, my brother!

(*Standing upright*)

Come now, let us arise. Carry Saul's and the Prince's
bodies back to the palace. Place them on a royal litter.
Let the whole people follow in procession; let them

accompany my grief with sobs and lamentations! You, musicians, sound a funeral march!

(They go out in procession to the accompaniment of a funeral march)

CURTAIN